THE PILOT
WHO WORE
A DRESS

Also by Tom Cutler

The First Da Capo Songbook (as Fred Plowright)
The Second Da Capo Songbook (as Fred Plowright)
Speak Well English (as Tomas Santos)
211 Things a Bright Boy Can Do
211 Things a Bright Girl Can Do (as Bunty Cutler)
A Gentleman's Bedside Book
Found in Translation (as Tomas Santos)
The Gentleman's Instant Genius Guide
A Little Bit of Slap and Tickle: The Unusual History of Sex and the People Who Have It

THE PILOT WHO WORE A DRESS

AND OTHER DASTARDLY LATERAL THINKING MYSTERIES

TOM CUTLER

HarperCollins*Publishers*

HarperCollins*Publishers*
1 London Bridge Street
London SE1 9GF

www.harpercollins.co.uk

First published by HarperCollins*Publishers* 2015

1 3 5 7 9 10 8 6 4 2

© Tom Cutler 2015

Illustrations © Bart Aalbers with the exception of
pp 147, 149, 152, 153, 155, 156, 157, 160, 161 © Alexei Penfold

Tom Cutler asserts the moral right to be
identified as the author of this work

A catalogue record of this book is
available from the British Library

HB ISBN 978-0-00-815721-0
EB ISBN 978-0-00-815720-3

Printed and bound in Great Britain by
Clays Ltd, St Ives plc

MIX
Paper from
responsible sources
FSC C007454
www.fsc.org

FSC™ is a non-profit international organisation established to promote
the responsible management of the world's forests. Products carrying the
FSC label are independently certified to assure consumers that they come
from forests that are managed to meet the social, economic and
ecological needs of present and future generations,
and other controlled sources.

Find out more about HarperCollins and the environment at
www.harpercollins.co.uk/green

This book is dedicated to Dr John H. Watson,
'the one fixed point in a changing age'.

'How often have I said to you that when you have eliminated the impossible, whatever remains, however improbable, must be the truth?'

Sherlock Holmes, in *The Sign of the Four* (1890),
by Arthur Conan Doyle

ABOUT THE AUTHOR

Tom Cutler began his career with numerous false starts, as a teacher, set designer, speechwriter, printer, wine waiter, City drone and radio reporter, before settling down in book and magazine publishing. After building up extensive scar tissue he finally threw caution to the wind and launched himself as a humorous writer upon a reading public that had done nothing to hurt him.

Tom's books cover a variety of subjects, including language, sex and music. Among his several international bestsellers are, *A Gentleman's Bedside Book* and the Amazon number-one blockbuster, *211 Things A Bright Boy Can Do*. His work has been translated into more languages than you can shake a stick at. Tom has written for the *Guardian*, the *Daily Mail*, the *Telegraph*, the *Huffington Post* and BBC radio, and he has a regular column in *The Chap* magazine.

He is a practising magician and member of the Magic Circle, as well as a detective story fan and longstanding Sherlock Holmes *aficionado*. A lifetime's experience as a very devious bugger has helped him in the writing of this book.

Tom lives at the seaside, where he enjoys kicking pebbles.

CONTENTS

LOCKED ROOMS AND IMPOSSIBLE MURDERS

LATERAL THINKING MYSTERIES FROM REAL LIFE

LATERAL THINKING BETCHAS AND GOTCHAS

THE SOLUTIONS

ACKNOWLEDGEMENTS

If you put your lateral thinking cap on you'll realise that the more people I put in my acknowledgments the more books I will sell. This is because everyone I mention will buy at least one copy as a souvenir, and more to give to their friends to make them envious. Maybe *The Book of Acknowledgements* will be the next big seller.

Anyway, I'd like to offer a genuine thank-you to the following people. First, my editor at HarperCollins, Jack Fogg, whose idea this book was, and who first approached me to write it. Second, my always-encouraging agent Laura Morris, for sensible advice, several disgraceful lunches, and at least one wild champagne party that I only dimly remember. Third, my illustrator Bart Aalbers, who has added an exuberant twang to the whole shebang.

Hats off to two old friends, Terry Guyatt, who first told me the story of the man with two girlfriends and gave me some early advice and encouragement, and John Kirby, for checking in regularly.

I thank my pal Chris Tuohy, who alerted me to the joke I used in 'The annoying computer password' mystery, and my new friend David Johnson, for sitting me down in the sunshine at the Yacht Club and listening to my early ideas. Cheers also to another new friend, Patricia Hammond, for sending me the most lovely and unexpected fan letter I've ever received.

I'm indebted to two excellent pub landlords, Richard at The Old Star and Mark at The Royal Sovereign, for providing me with old-fashioned liquid cheer when I was at low tide. I compliment Rob Sr and Rob Jr, Frank and Matt, and Richard, on their hard work, and I especially thank Arthur, for his zest, good humour, craftsmanship and strange unearthly whistling. His 'Greensleeves' is like something out of *The Twilight Zone*.

I'm grateful to the experts in the Magic Circle library, and at West Sussex Libraries, for providing, in the first case, information, and, in the second, refuge when the six people in the previous paragraph were making too much noise.

This book would have been a shadow of itself without the inspiring work of the towering Martin Gardner: mathematician, magician, sceptic, wit, puzzle collector and abundant author. I commend Michael Howell and Peter Ford for their superb 1985 page-turner, *The Ghost Disease and Twelve Other Stories of Detective Work in the Medical Field*, which filled me in on the Epping Jaundice, the Euston Road poisonings and the mysterious ailment that felled Clare Boothe Luce. I bow down also to Paul Sloane and Des MacHale, whose years of painstaking collecting and publishing of lateral thinking puzzles helped me track down some of the quirkiest, and I propose a resounding three cheers to those anonymous geniuses who came up with them all in the first place.

Finally, I thank Marianne, as usual, for everything.

FOREWORD

When people talk of the 'Golden Age' of crime fiction they're usually referring to the 1920s and 30s, but some authorities believe that we are currently going through another 'Golden Age'. The range, profile and quality of contemporary crime fiction are probably as high as they have ever been.

But one thing the current Golden Age lacks – which was very much present in the previous one – is a sense of fun.

As embittered middle-aged Inspectors with drink and relationship problems try to identify serial killers, as forensic pathologists sift through decomposing organs, and as dour Scandinavian detectives confront the unalterable bleakness of human existence, crime fiction has lost its traditional link with high spirits. *Noir* is the new black, and that's just something readers have to take on board.

I'm sure, at universities all over the world, doctorates are even now being written about the reasons for this change. Whodunits in which the puzzle was paramount came to a natural end because there were no more puzzles left that hadn't already been done. The country houses, perfectly designed for weekend house parties for guests with 'dark secrets in their past' and offering a wonderful range of domestics to act as witnesses, informants and suspects, did not survive the Second World War. No longer could their owners 'get the staff', and many were converted into hotels, boys' prep schools and secret military training centres.

The great carnage of the war also made the Golden Age tradition of treating death as a kind of parlour game seem a little tasteless. Publications like *The Baffle Book*, a collection of murder puzzles very popular in the 1930s, appeared to be offensively trivial.

Another development, the abolition of the death penalty in 1965, meant crime novels were left with a lot more loose ends to be unravelled. No longer could the pointing finger of Hercule Poirot at the perpetrator in the library signal the permanent end of a case, with the hangman's noose tying everything up in a neat bow. What had been black and white moved on to a colour-chart of greys.

So it was no surprise that crime fiction grew darker.

I'm sure I'm not alone in slightly regretting that change. 'Murder as parlour game' still holds a strong attraction, and it is no surprise how many books from the original Golden Age are now being successfully reprinted. Murder Mystery Dinners are a hugely popular form of entertainment, and new generations of young people are introduced every day to the fun of Cluedo.

It is firmly within that tradition of having fun with crime that this book by Tom Cutler fits. He has taken the original idea of selecting lateral thinking challenges and writing them up as mini detective stories, then asking the reader to work out the solution. The Crime Puzzle Book, thought to be dead after 1939, has been reborn in a new form for the 21st century.

I'm sure a great many readers will relish the challenges that it presents to them.

Simon Brett
Crime Writers' Association Diamond Dagger award-winner
and President of the Detection Club

INTRODUCTION

Two men are playing tennis together. After an exhausting three-set match, both of them win. How can this be? All will be explained in a moment.

The reason lateral thinking problems are so tricky, and such fun to solve, is that we tend to think in a routine way. Our ingrained habits, inhibitions and false assumptions hinder us in winkling out the less apparent possibilities tucked away inside the lateral thinking shell. But if we can look at the problem from another perspective, the answer often pops out. As Sherlock Holmes tells Dr Watson, 'When once your point of view is changed the very thing which was so damning becomes a clue to the truth.'

It's like the joke about the man who dies and goes to hell. He sees an ugly old villain making love to a beautiful young blonde. When he objects that this is hardly a harsh enough fate, the Devil replies, 'Who are you to question that woman's punishment?'

The term 'lateral thinking' was coined in 1967 by a man who liked to use an overhead projector named Edward de Bono (the man is named Edward de Bono, not the projector). Edward de Bono has said that the mind can see only what it is prepared to see, but that we can solve some otherwise tricky problems if we look at things from the side – which is what 'lateral' means.

For example, if we hear that Dr Alex Bernard is a vicar we will probably make several unconscious assumptions about him. But, as Sherlock Holmes also said, 'There is nothing more deceptive than an obvious fact,' for Dr Alex Bernard is a *woman*. Thinking that a vicar named Alex is a man is not sexism, as some people would insist, but just a forgivable mistake, because if we didn't make assumptions based on our experience of the way the world normally works we would be so abstract that we wouldn't be able to laugh at jokes or get on with people at parties.

In this book I've decided to make the most of the combination of riddle and story that most lateral thinking problems embody. Solving these mysteries won't require unusual intelligence or imagination, and all the information you need is there in the tale – though the solution may be hidden in plain sight by the way in which the puzzle has been framed. There is no cheating, but there is, of course, a fair sprinkling of red herrings.

The first section of the book contains celebrated standards from the lateral thinking hall of fame. There's everything from the immortal 'Man in the lift' to the baffling 'Murder in the snow', along with some less familiar, and a few entirely original, problems.

It is a feature of lateral thinking mysteries that they involve lots of death and destruction, with a fair number of hangings, shootings and suicides. What is so alluring about all this violence I can't say, but I've kept it all in, along with a few laughs, I hope.

Besides the classics, I've included a section featuring some of the finest 'locked-room' mysteries and 'impossible' crimes from detective fiction, adapted to the lateral thinking format. Some of the very best head-scratchers from masters such as Lord Dunsany and Arthur Conan Doyle are included.

A Real Life section features mysterious true events such as the curious case of the *Mary Celeste*, the dihydrogen monoxide affair and the riddle of the Epping Jaundice.

Finally, there is a part featuring bar betchas and gotchas, with lateral thinking matchstick puzzles, counter-intuitive gags and unlosable bets.

The Pilot Who Wore a Dress makes great solo reading but you can also use it to challenge a roomful of players. You can even pass the book round and take turns reading out the stories. Apart from the monkey business behind the betchas, which is included with the bet, you will discover the fun and quirky solutions to the mysteries in their own section at the back of the book. They are as compelling as the enigmas they explain.

I hope you find these lateral thinking mysteries as much fun to solve as I did to write. *Good luck.*

Oh, by the way, if you're still wondering about those two tennis players, the answer is that they are partners playing a doubles match. *Of course!*

LATERAL THINKING CLASSICS

'These little grey cells. It is up to them.'
Agatha Christie

THE SAILOR WHO ATE THE CREAM TEA

The mystery

On the western outskirts of Plymouth lies the little seaside town of St Havet. It has a striped lighthouse, a rocky foreshore and a few red cliffs, which fossil-hunters say are a goldmine of echinoids and ammonites.

The town's pretty high street has the tang of salt in its nostrils, and several old-fashioned shops line the cobbled roadway: a haberdashery, a fishmonger's where the gulls circle, and a greengrocer's. There is a friendly pub, The Lion and Lobster, and a charming tearoom – Marianne's – famous for its homemade clotted cream and giant scones. The tearoom boasts lace tablecloths, an excitement of doilies, and those things that look like three flying saucers on a stick, which they put cakes on at teatime. On the walls hang faded photographs of the skiffs of Worlock's Hole.

One afternoon, not long ago, the bell on the door of Marianne's tearoom tinkled brightly. A young man walked in and sat down in the sunshine by the window. He was the only customer. Daisy, the waitress, daughter of the late Marianne,

and now sole owner of the establishment, greeted him with a warm smile.

After consulting the dainty menu for a minute the man caught her eye again. She approached the table and asked him what he would like. 'One of your famous cream teas, please,' he said.

Daisy wrote this down carefully in her notebook and bustled off to the kitchen, emerging in due course with a steaming brown teapot, and a blue cup and saucer from a different tea service. She handed her customer his pot of tea and retired again to the kitchen. After a minute she was back, staggering under a tray laden with two scones the size of half-bricks, half a pint of strawberry jam in a pretty bowl with a silver spoon, and a saucer piled high with yellow clotted cream.

With an air of great deliberation, the man removed the scones from the plate and, using the spoon, distributed exactly twelve dollops of cream around the circumference of the plate. He carefully placed a dollop of jam between each blob of cream. In the centre of the plate he placed a scone, which he carefully cut into four pieces, before slicing the second scone in half and putting it on the plate. He poured himself a cup of tea and painstakingly dunked the small pieces of quartered scone in the tea before eating them, one after the other. He dipped the two halves of the remaining scone in the jam, and then in the cream, going around the plate like a clock face, but he took care not to dunk them in his tea.

Daisy had been watching the man carefully and she approached the table. 'So, Sir,' she said, 'I see you are a sailor.'

The problem

How did Daisy know that her customer with the curious eating habits was a sailor?

Solution on page 181.

THE WISHING CUP OF KERIPUT

The mystery

Sir Humphrey Bumfreigh (1873–1979) was an Egyptologist and explorer who became famous around the world for his discovery in 1922 of the desert tomb of King Orang Tua Keriput.

His adventure began in 1913, when the wealthy aristocrat Lord Elpus employed Bumfreigh to supervise his ambitious efforts to find the Keriput tomb, whose whereabouts had until that time eluded archaeologists. They began excavations in the Valley of the Wasps on the east bank of the Nile, near Thebes (modern-day Luxor). But in January 1921, after eight expensive years of finding nothing but quite a lot of sand, Bumfreigh was

told by Lord Elpus that he had one last chance to discover the lost tomb before he turned off the money tap at the end of the year.

It looked hopeless, but on 6 December 1921 Humphrey Bumfreigh made the find of his life. While scraping dispiritedly around the bottom of an old wall, he uncovered four large stone steps. Some hieroglyphs on the steps suggested to him that this was the top of a staircase leading down to King Keriput's tomb.

Bumfreigh immediately sent Lord Elpus an excited wire begging him to come, and on 11 January 1922, with Elpus at his elbow, and using a knife that his grandmother had given him for his sixteenth birthday, Bumfreigh made 'a bit of a hole up near the top of this old door', and was able to peek into the room behind. By the light of a flickering candle he could see gold and ebony artefacts which had been placed there before the time of Jesus, and which he was the first man to see for more than 2,000 years.

The tomb proved to be more spectacular even than King Tut's, and over the next few years thousands of objects were cleared and many were sold off to collectors and museums. The Egyptian locals warned of 'the curse of the pharaohs', which would, they claimed, be visited at once upon violators of the tomb. But Humphrey Bumfreigh's death in 1979, from a seizure brought on by kissing one of his team of nurses at the age of 106, seemed not to bear this out.

Perhaps the most mysterious of the Keriput finds was discovered in the sand in front of the steps to the tomb. More modern than the ancient relics, it was a plain ceramic pot, which the press dubbed the Wishing Cup of Keriput. Around its rim it bore a mysterious Latin-looking inscription that read: ITI SAPIS SPOTANDA BIGO NÉ. Neither Sir Humphrey Bumfreigh, Lord Elpus, nor anybody else could make anything of it, and the great explorer went to his death not knowing what it meant.

_____

The problem

Can you decipher the mysterious inscription around the top of the Wishing Cup of Keriput?

Solution on page 181.

MURDER IN THE SNOW

The mystery

Known as the 'Big Freeze', the winter of 1962/63 was one of the coldest and longest British winters ever documented. December had started foggy and London was in the middle of what would turn out to be its last pea-souper. Halfway through the month a cold snap brought snow, causing people to ready themselves for a white Christmas. They began in earnest to shop for presents.

It continued bitterly cold for the rest of Advent and over the Christmas holiday. Persistently heavy snow fell on Boxing Day and into the following day, as delighted children threw snow-balls at their guffawing uncles.

By the end of the month a savage blizzard was sweeping across the country. Freezing gales sculpted the snow into twenty-foot drifts, blocking roads and burying steam trains up to their shoulders.

Wythenshawe in Cheshire was particularly badly hit, and it was here, on 20 January, that the papers reported a disturbing occurrence that had diverted the authorities from their road-clearing, burst-pipe-repairing and train-excavating duties.

Imagine the scene: the body of a man, dressed in a heavy coat over layers of clothing, has been spotted in the middle of a snow-covered field by some children coming home from school for their lunch. One of them, Charlie Shaver, braver perhaps than the rest, crosses the field to look at the body. The man's face has been blasted away by something like a sawn-off shot-gun, a weapon typical in country post office robberies around these parts. He is on his back in the snow, which is stained pink with his blood. There is no sign of a weapon.

Charlie races to the other side of the field and knocks on the door of his auntie, Ada Ferribridge. Ada, who had heard a single gunshot ring out about twenty minutes earlier, at once calls the police, who, keen to get away from shovelling their station forecourt, arrive at the scene with a good deal of important fuss.

They immediately recognise the body as that of local charmer and ladies' man Raymond Trethewey. His manicured nails and fancy tattoo are known to all the regulars in the pub. Photographs are taken and the body is removed.

The autopsy report describes a short, very slight young fellow, in good nick but minus his appendix. He has died from a shotgun blast fired from below his chin, which has removed his previously handsome face.

Trethewey, it seems, had been on his way to the Cross In Hand pub in the high street, where he always goes for a lunch-time glass of beer with his next-door-neighbour and friend, the blacksmith Jack Ferrario. But today he hadn't turned up.

Apart from young Charlie's footprints going towards and away from the body, there is only one other set of marks, quickly identified as footprints made by the wellington boots habitually worn by Trethewey. These are expensive, specially commissioned boots. Though they look like normal wellingtons they have on their sole a handmade tread incorporating the victim's initials, *RWT*.

Trethewy's distinctive boot prints start at his front door and continue unbroken to the middle of the field, where his body lay. They are easy to track because of the monogram, which, up to the position of the dead body, has been very heavily trodden into the deep snow.

But none of this makes sense, because Trethewey is not wearing his famous boots. He has on instead a pair of totally unsuitable moccasins. Furthermore, the boot prints continue from the body in an unbroken line into a copse of trees between the field and the village high street, where they disappear, the snow having not penetrated the overgrown wood. Even odder, the prints beyond the body appear somewhat lighter and less deep, though still heavy enough.

The local police are quick to spot the problems. How can a man in light shoes walk into the middle of a field, leaving boot tracks, shoot himself in the face, and then continue on his merry way, taking his weapon with him?

Stirring a mug of Ada Ferribridge's steaming tea, Sergeant Swainston remarks that the prints might actually be those of the murderer, who stealthily approached Trethewey, his feet muffled by the snow, shot him, and then continued into the wood, there disposing of the firearm. 'So where are the victim's footprints, then?' asks a young constable, passing round some of Ada's biscuits. To this Swainston has no answer so he strolls over to the pub to relieve himself of the several teas he has had that afternoon.

As he is emerging from the gents an old man in a cap motions him across. He tells Swainston that the previous day, as today, Trethewey was wearing nothing more than very wet moccasins on his feet, despite the deep snow. He says he had claimed that his boots had been stolen from outside his front door. But he has more …

Two days previously Jack Ferrario had blown his top in the pub, apparently furious that his next-door-neighbour Trethewey had been hopping over their party wall and romancing Ferrario's wife while he was shoeing horses at the smithy. Ferrario promised that he was going to damage Trethewey's good looks in a way he wouldn't be able to fix.

The old chap says that though Ferrario has small feet he is a huge ox of a man and that if he decided to pick up the slight Trethewey, carry him round the pub, and then fling him through the etched-glass window, he'd be able to do it without any trouble.

A light springs up in Swainston's eye.

The problem

Who has killed Trethewey and where is the weapon? Is blacksmith Ferrario the murderer? If so how did he shoot the victim in the middle of a snow-covered field without leaving any footprints? Where are Trethewey's boots, why was he wearing moccasins, and why are there no moccasin prints in the field?

Finally, why has such a slight man made such heavy impressions with his monogrammed wellies?

Solution on page 181.

THE YORKSHIRE FACTORY

The mystery

It is a September day in 1925, on the outskirts of a small Yorkshire town tucked into a quiet nook in the Dales. It is lunchtime and the bells from the moorland church are chiming the quarter. Coming over the bridge is a solitary walker dressed in hiking tweeds, his cap pulled down over his eyes against the rain, which is now coming on hard. Across the high street he spies a cosy pub where he decides to shelter and have a bite to eat.

Inside the pub, our walker, whose name is Gerald, shakes the rain from his cap and hangs it on a peg beside the fire. He orders a pint of beer and a piece of cheese from the rosy-faced landlady and looking around the low ceilinged room he spots in the corner an old man in a straw hat, nursing a drink in a china mug.

Gerald leans his stick against the chimney corner and goes over to sit beside the old man. 'Good afternoon,' he says.

'Aye', replies the man, taking a pull at his ale and drawing a rough sleeve across his muttonchop whiskers.

Through the window Gerald can see, on the other side of a dry-stone wall, a huge Victorian factory building and its handsome reflection in the millstream. A plume of smoke rises from the chimney, and the factory name, S. GARTONS, is reflected in gigantic back-to-front capitals in the water. The old man removes the long clay pipe from his lips and says, 'You're not from round here, are you?'

'No,' replies Gerald.

The man pauses. 'I'll tell you what, lad,' he says. 'If you can tell me in one guess what it is they make in that factory I'll buy you as much beer as you can drink. If you fail, you'll do the same for me. One guess only.' Gerald muses for a minute, staring into the shimmering water of the millstream opposite.

'Well, I've no idea,' he says. Then he takes a longer look at the name reflected in the water. 'All right,' he says suddenly, 'I'll tell you.'

The old man grins. 'What is it then?'

'Handkerchiefs!' exclaims Gerald.

'You cheated! You knew already,' gasps the man.

'No I didn't,' says Gerald. 'It was easy.'

_____

The problem

How did Gerald know what was made in the factory?

Solution on page 182.

THE RIDDLE OF THE BURNS SUPPER

The mystery

John and Joan Jones live in a charming 18th-century cottage near Matlock in Derbyshire, on the south-eastern cusp of the Peak District. From their bedroom windows their two children Julie and Jeremy often look out across the craggy sheep-sprinkled vista, which stretches from the low screen of evergreen trees at the bottom of their back garden out as far as the eye can see.

They watch the ravens circling and cawing overhead, tearing worms from the damp earth, or dropping snails from a height onto the limestone outcrops as if cracking nuts. At night a low wind is often to be heard moaning under the eaves and rattling the handle of the Joneses' garden shed.

The Joneses are a happy family. John Jones is a Scotsman who teaches business studies at Buxton's Espurio University. Joan Jones is a full-time mother. Their cheerful children catch the bus to school every day and are both doing well. Jeremy is good at drawing and Julie likes maths. They help their mother around the house but from time to time Jeremy is mischievous, blowing raspberries at the dustmen through a hole in the hedge or letting his beagle Tinker off the lead when he goes into town.

One Sunday morning Mr and Mrs Jones return home in the early hours after a roisterous Burns Night supper in town.

Letting themselves into the house in the pitch black, they relieve the babysitter and push straight off to bed.

Mrs Jones wakes later than usual the next morning. She had rather more sparkling wine than she'd meant to the previous night and John polished off a bottle of malt whisky with a couple of friends. Today her head is throbbing and he is snoring for Scotland.

Mrs Jones gingerly opens the bedroom curtains to take a look at the morning. The sun is streaming onto the front lawn and it is a good deal warmer than it has been over the past week, which is nice.

But Joan notices something unusual. Lying on the wet lawn are some objects that she cannot identify. Pulling on her dressing gown, she goes downstairs and turns on the kettle in the kitchen before padding over to the front door. She opens it a crack to have a better look at the things on the grass.

In the middle of the lawn are eleven pieces of coal, each very roughly the size of a walnut. They are not far apart and appear to have been placed together deliberately. Lying nearby all on its own is a large carrot, which a raven is eyeing from the wall. Somebody, presumably the person who placed the other objects on the lawn, has left his or her scarf on the grass, and it is now soaking wet. The scarf is of a very common design and looks rather moth-eaten. It certainly isn't one Mrs Jones would allow John or Jeremy to wear in a similar state.

Behind her, Joan Jones hears the tread of Jeremy on the stairs. His hair is up on end and he is holding a jam jar with a snail in it. 'Malcolm wants some lettuce,' says Jeremy.

'Good morning to you too,' says his mother, shutting the door. 'I hope you were good last night.'

'Suzanne let us watch *The Exorcist*,' says Jeremy. Joan makes a mental note to think twice about the suitability of Suzanne as a babysitter next time.

'What do you know about those things on the lawn?' says Mrs

Jones suspiciously, swallowing a couple of aspirin and pouring boiling water into two mugs. 'Did you put them on the lawn?' Jeremy smiles and shakes his head. He pours some sugar-coated breakfast cereal into a bowl and adds nearly a pint of milk and a good deal more sugar. 'What about Julie?' asks his mum.

'No,' replies Jeremy with his mouth full, 'she didn't put them on the lawn either. Nobody did.'

Mrs Jones is bemused but doesn't fancy an argument. She also decides against breakfast. 'Not too much noise this morning, darling,' she tells her son. 'Your father had a busy day yesterday.' She carries the coffee cups upstairs, trying, between hiccups, to solve the mystery of the strange objects arranged on her lawn.

The problem

Jeremy was telling the truth. Nobody put the strange assortment of objects on the Joneses' lawn. But there is a very straightforward reason why they are there. What is it?

Solution on page 182.

THE ANNOYING COMPUTER PASSWORD

The mystery

Children these days seem to have little trouble remembering twenty computer passwords, yet they still cannot remember the kings and queens of England. Why should they, when they can look them up on their iPhone?

Older people often have trouble remembering where they live and their own names, let alone recalling their PIN number, mobile number, telephone banking security questions and all that stuff.

I don't know who is responsible for the following joke about computers – I wish I did – but it kind of sums up the situation.

COMPUTER: Please enter your new password.
USER: cabbage
COMPUTER: Sorry, the password must be more than 8 characters.
USER: boiled cabbage
COMPUTER: Sorry, the password must contain 1 numerical character.
USER: 1 boiled cabbage
COMPUTER: Sorry, the password cannot have blank spaces.
USER: 50fuckingboiledcabbages
COMPUTER: Sorry, the password must contain at least one upper-case character.
USER: 50FUCKINGboiledcabbages
COMPUTER: Sorry, the password cannot use more than one upper-case character consecutively.
USER: 50FuckingBoiledCabbagesShovedUpYourArseIfY ouDon'tGiveMeAccessNow!
COMPUTER: Sorry, the password cannot contain punctuation.
USER: ReallyPissedOff50FuckingBoiledCabbages ShovedUpYourArseIfYouDontGiveMeAccessNow
COMPUTER: Sorry, that password is already in use.

Anyway, the point is to tell you about a man named Bill, who could never remember how to spell his password. He was alert, sane, and happy with computers, but spelling had always been a bit tricky for him. It wasn't just unusual words like 'acquit' and 'minuscule' that gave him trouble, it was ordinary words with double letters, like 'misspell' – some-what ironically.

The most annoying of the lot was his password, which he never could spell correctly, so that he spent many wasted hours trying to log on to his computer.

The problem

How did Bill spell his password?

Solution on page 183.

TERRY'S GIRLFRIENDS

The mystery

Terry is a young man with two girlfriends: Emma, who lives to his east, and Wendy, who lives to his west. Emma East is a petite and sultry redhead; Wendy West is a blonde volcano – cool on the outside but bubbling hot below the surface ice. Terry likes both girls equally and enjoys the company of one just as much as the other.

Terry's local railway station has only one platform. It is one of those 'island' platforms of the sort where trains on one side always go one way and trains on the other side always go the opposite way. There is an unfailingly reliable hourly service in each direction, east and west, the trains always run on time, there are the same number both ways, and no train is ever cancelled. (You'll have noticed that this is very unlike the real world.)

Unfortunately, Terry is completely disorganised, with no idea of the actual times of either service. In one respect this doesn't

matter, because Terry's girlfriends never go out. They are so devoted to him that they're always at home in their respective houses, looking out of their front window, waiting for him to visit.

Every time Terry fancies some female company he leaves home without consulting a watch or clock, goes straight to the station, buys a ticket valid to either station, runs up the steps to the middle of the island platform, and boards the first train that comes in, whether eastbound or westbound. There's one of each every hour and they are perfectly normal trains in every way. He catches his trains at random times and on random days. Sometimes he gets there late in the evening. Sometimes it's early morning. Sometimes it's lunchtime, sometimes teatime. He arrives on any and every day of the week in no particular order and he goes either east or west according to which train arrives first.

The westbound train, going to Wendy, leaves at exactly the same time past each hour. The eastbound 'Emma' train does the same but leaves at a different time from the westbound 'Wendy' train, so Terry is never torn between the two.

The problem

Last year Terry saw Emma East a lot, and many more times than he saw Wendy West. In fact, he hardly saw Wendy West at all. Why?

Solution on page 183.

THE LORRY DRIVER SLAYING

The mystery

The Sting is a 1973 film starring Paul Newman and Robert Redford. It covers the ups and downs of two confidence tricksters as they try their hand at everything from racing scams to cheating at cards. There are several other successful films on the same subject, which makes you wonder what it is about conmen and card-sharps that provides this mysterious allure.

The most polished card cheats are very skilled and slick. You've got the 'mechanics', who use sleight of hand such as second dealing, whereby the top card is retained on the pack by the thumb while the second card is invisibly slipped out under it in the process of the deal. Then there are the 'stackers', who can arrange the cards in a useful order while shuffling. There are the 'paper players', who use marked cards, and there are 'hand muckers', who cleverly conceal cards in their palms and switch them for other more useful cards during play.

Most amateur cheats keep things simple, using less compli-cated methods such as 'shorting the pot' (quietly putting in less money for their bet than they say) or peeking at other players' cards. The benefit of the simple approach is deniability.

A fine example of suspected cheating of the sophisticated sort came one chilly December day in 2011 at a roadside café near Newcastle, where a group of lorry drivers had finished their egg and chips and were playing a game of poker.

The game had been going some time and the pot was huge. The card players were all experienced, and very good at what they were doing. There was no chat and the focus was on the game. Cards were held close to chests and mugs of tea were going cold. Glances passed back and forth, but the stony poker faces gave nothing away.

Several players clearly thought they had good hands, and betting was serious. A great wad of money had built up in the centre of the table. Then came the moment. The dealer laid down, in dramatic fashion, one card at a time, a perfect royal flush in Spades: Ten, Jack, Queen, King and Ace, the strongest possible poker hand, and an unlikely one.

For a moment a hush fell upon the group. The dealer's face showed no emotion. Outside, the engines of arriving vehicles appeared to fall silent. Then one of the men, large and broad-shouldered, stood up, knocking his metal chair onto the tile floor. 'You're a cheat!' he announced determinedly, aiming a stout forefinger at the dealer. 'And I can prove it.' The dealer didn't speak but instead, in front of a whole table of witnesses, silently drew a long knife and stabbed the man through the chest, killing him on the spot.

The café owner locked himself into his room and immediately called the police, who arrived quickly. As a trickle of blood continued to run from the table into the spreading red pool on the floor they interviewed all the lorry drivers and also the café owner. All the men agreed on the dealer's guilt and even the dealer admitted the stabbing, though not the cheating.

But, after hours of questioning, a confession, and clear evidence that the dealer was guilty of the murder of an innocent card player, not a single man was arrested – not even for illegal gambling – and every one of them was allowed to walk free and drive his lorry home.

_____

The problem

Why, when the police had the dealer's confession and the agreement of everyone around the table on the dealer's guilt, did the police let every single man off scot-free?

Solution on page 184.

THE MAGIC BUCKET

The mystery

Stuart O'Brien is a successful businessman, with silvering hair, a flash car and an imposingly ugly mansion in the Surrey countryside.

Stuart left school without taking any exams but used his persuasive skills to land himself a job in the sales team of Polyplastika, a plastics manufacturer. The company turns out drainpipes, washing-up bowls, industrial pallets and buckets by the thousand.

Stuart was always a fantastic salesman and rose through the company ranks very fast. His friends call him 'Irish Stu', and say that he hasn't so much kissed the Blarney Stone as stuck his tongue down its throat. By the time he was twenty Stu was heading the firm's sales team and was beginning to earn serious money.

Stu is now strengthening the firm's toehold in China, he's on the company board and is being tipped as the firm's next CEO. He plays golf to a handicap of four, buys the most expensive

foreign colognes and has just treated himself to a pair of enormous Tudor garage doors. Life is good.

Stu is married to Laverne, a tall blonde with an expensive taste in handbags and holidays. She has a mouth full of uncannily white teeth, which flash like urinals in a cave.

Apart from looking good on Stu's arm at company dos and trips to the Far East, Laverne is a great party-giver. At their annual summer barbecue, held at the O'Briens' vast Surrey home, Laverne circulates in the garden in unlikely heels, topping people up by the pool, putting little umbrellas in their glasses, and doling out to each of them at least eleven seconds of her white-urinal smile. And it's at the barbie that Stu always does his party piece.

Someone hands him one of the company's famous plastic buckets – he prefers to use a red one. He then hands back the lid, which he doesn't need, and fills the bucket to the very brim with warmish water. He now asks for silence while he slowly turns the bucket upside down. It remains full. Not a drop spills out. He doesn't swing it round his head, add anything to it, or put anything on the top – it's an open bucket full of nothing but water. To prove the point, he puts his hand into the upside-down bucket and brings it out wet, shaking and flicking a few drops at his friends.

After a couple of seconds, or longer if people ask, he turns the bucket right-way up again. It contains just as much water as it did at the start. He hands it to Laverne, who can barely hold it because it's still full to the brim.

Stu's audience are so astonished by his performance that many laugh in sheer disbelief, and, if they didn't know it before, realise that Irish Stu is one of the best showmen going.

Finally, with the help of someone else, because it's heavy, Laverne empties the water out of the bucket onto Stu's head, producing a round of applause and shouts of glee. Stu then dries himself off and goes in to change.

If people want, they can examine the bucket at any time (Stu has been known to sell a couple during this procedure).

———————————

The problem

How on earth can Irish Stu turn a full, lidless bucket of water upside-down in his back garden without the water pouring out?

Solution on page 184.

THE IMPOSSIBLE BROTHERS

The mystery

Bob and Jim are brothers. Bob was born in Hastane Maternity Hospital, near Drumroos in Scotland, at 8.15 a.m. on April Fools' Day 1976. Jim was born in the same place, just seven minutes later.

Their mum remembers the day not only because of the happy occasion of their births but because of the Jovian–Plutonian gravitational effect that astronomer Patrick Moore reported would happen that day.

Jupiter is the largest planet in the solar system, with a mass of about two and a half times that of all the other planets glued together. Pluto on the other hand is so small that in 2006 it was reclassified as a dwarf planet.

Moore told listeners to BBC radio that as Pluto passed behind Jupiter at 9.47 that morning, a powerful combination of the two planets' gravitation would decrease the gravity on Earth. People were told that if they jumped in the air at exactly the right time they would stay up longer than normal and briefly feel as if they were floating.

Shortly after the appointed time hundreds of listeners telephoned the BBC to report that they had indeed felt the effect. One woman said that she and some friends had been 'wafted' from their chairs and 'orbited gently around the room'. Not that you can orbit around a room when you're inside it, but never mind. (*These people actually vote.*)

Of course, the whole thing was an April Fools' hoax by the mischievous Patrick Moore. Although Jupiter is very massive, it is also a very long long way away. At its closest to Earth the planet has a gravitational pull only about the same as that of a Renault Twizy on an old man standing a couple of feet away. The gravitational attraction of Pluto is even less. It's about the same as a marble 100 yards away from you. Which means that even the combined gravity of the two distant planets is far too small to cause a person to become lighter or float while jumping. It's a good job that gravity is such a weak force, or the gravitational pull of Bob and Jim's obstetrician would have caused the tide to go out in their mum's cup of tea.

The problem

Jim and Bob were born at the same place in the same hour of the same day of the same month of the same year, and to the same mother. Yet they are not twins. How can this be?

Solution on page 184.

ARMS AND THE CHILD

The mystery

Jenny Brown and Margaret Green are lifelong friends. They grew up together, they went to the same school together, and they graduated from teacher-training college together. Both of them applied for a teaching post at their local village primary and they were appointed at the same time, in the same September of the same year.

Jenny and Margaret now teach in that school, in adjacent classrooms. The school is a charming Victorian building with a steep tiled roof, and roses round the door. It smells, as many schools do, of shepherd's pie and pine disinfectant. It has about 120 children each year and at the end of their four years most of them feed into the large secondary school in the town.

Jenny and Margaret's school is a happy place, with a good head, good staff, generous playgrounds, a large sports field and plenty of trees. Not so long ago a local supermarket offered a great deal of money to buy the bottom end of the cricket pitch, but the headmistress, Miss Jean Piaget, had other ideas. The parents carried her in triumph on the day the supermarket abandoned its scheme (they carried her metaphorically, that is).

One day the two young teachers were sipping tea in the staffroom and discussing mathematics. They decided to teach their pupils that maths is not just for passing exams but is a useful and fascinating subject in the real world. They devised a lesson plan in which the children in their classes would measure the length of every child's arms and deal with the numbers in different ways, to arrive at the three different sorts of average: the mean (got by adding up all the different lengths of the children's arms and dividing this figure by the number of children in the class), the median (arrived at by listing in order the different lengths of the children's arms and finding which arm length falls in the middle of the list) and the mode (found by seeing which arm length occurs most often).

On Monday morning Jenny and Margaret called their respective registers. There were 28 children present in each class, with no absences.

They then explained the task to their classes and allowed them to decide who would be in charge of the tape measure, who would take down all the measurements and who would check the figures before handing in the final calculations. The children got to work, and by lunchtime the numbers were all written down.

In the staffroom Jenny and Margaret compared lists and checked the maths. Miss Tijdelijk, a temporary supply teacher, was passing through with a sandwich and asked Margaret and Jenny what they were doing. They showed her the numbers and to her utter astonishment she discovered that, although everything had been done in exactly the same way in both classrooms, and although all the measurements were correct and all the mathematics properly done, the average (mean) arm length of the children in Jenny's class was three inches greater than the mean arm length of the children in Margaret's class.

The problem

The children in both classes are all physically normal, and nobody in either class has extraordinarily short or long arms. The arithmetic is correct and, in fact, accurately reflects the actual arm lengths of the children.

How is it that the children in Jenny's class appear to have significantly longer arms than the children in Margaret's class?

Solution on page 184.

THE WINDOW CLEANER IN THE SKY

The mystery

Tall buildings are nothing new. Blocks of high-rise flats were all the rage in Ancient Rome, where they rose to a height of ten or more storeys. Some Roman emperors took against them, though, getting their togas in a right tangle trying to set a height limit on the pesky things, but without much luck. If an emperor can't get something like that done it makes you wonder about your own planning department down at the town hall.

It wasn't just Rome, either. Twelfth-century Bologna had many high-rise apartment blocks too, something like 180 of them. It looked like an ancient New York. The tallest of these buildings – which hasn't fallen down over the centuries – is the Asinelli Tower, one of the so-called *Duo Torri* (Two Towers) that together resemble the old World Trade Center. The Asinelli

Tower is 319 feet high, and I can imagine the 12th-century Bolognese sitting down to eat their spaghetti at sunset, grumpily looking out over the red roofs of the city and writing endless letters to the council to complain about being overlooked.

But neither the Roman nor the Bolognese towers were really skyscrapers. This term was first used in the late 19th century to describe steel-frame buildings of ten storeys or more. Nowadays it can refer to any very tall multi-storey building, most often one covered in big windows.

The oldest iron-frame building in the world, and the grandfather of the skyscraper, is the Maltings in Shrewsbury, which went up in 1797. However, as with the Roman tower blocks, there were complaints. And it was the same in 19th-century London, when a British empress took a leaf out of the Roman emperors' book.

Queen Victoria, Empress of India, had a really good moan about tall buildings going up near Buckingham Palace, and to mollify the monarch height limits were introduced, which continued to be enforced until the 1950s. Prince Charles carries on the good fight today in an effort to prevent the building of ugly high-rise buildings in London, and pushing to have The Gherkin thatched. I've noticed that, rather like the Romans, he's not having much luck.

Many office employees today work in skyscrapers, and one of the benefits is the fun of watching the guys who clean the windows from special cradles trying to cope with the high winds, and being stared at.

It was in 2012 that Horace Morris, an experienced 60-year-old window cleaner who was working on a window on the 40th floor of the 94-storey Alto Tower, near London Bridge, had a spot of trouble. Horace was smoking a cigarette and whistling along to the radio. He had cleaned the windows many times before and was not really paying proper attention to what he was doing.

As he was reaching across to get to a particularly dirty patch in a tricky corner, Horace slipped off his support and fell.

—————

The problem

Horace was not wearing any kind of safety harness or other device, just his workwear. His clothes were not padded, he had no safety hat – or any hat – and there was nothing to slow his fall. Yet when he hit the ground Horace merely shook his head, rubbed his sore hands together, and stood up. He had broken no bones, and had only a slight scratch to his palm, a sore knuckle, a bent thumb and two very achy knees. How come?

Solution on page 185.

THE TROUBLESOME SIGNPOST

The mystery

Everybody who is old enough to remember the event recalls where he or she was when President Kennedy was shot, or when the World Trade Center was attacked. For those who witnessed its aftermath, the Great Storm of 1987 is another of those memorable events.

During the night of 15 October violent hurricane-force winds tore roofs off houses in London, demolished the seven oaks in Sevenoaks, and blew beach huts half a mile across the sea road in Hove. Roads and railways blocked by downed trees kept commuters at home, and fallen electricity lines left many without power. London, East Anglia and the Home Counties were particularly badly hit, being buffeted by winds the like of which will probably not be felt again for another 200 years. Gorleston in Norfolk chalked up a gust of 122 mph.

I remember this all as if it was yesterday. I was living in Muswell Hill, in North London. As I walked through the woods to the Tube station the next morning – I was meant to travel to Sussex – I had to step over branches and jump over whole trees. No trains were moving so I postponed my visit until the following week. When Monday arrived I set off on my journey.

I enjoy the countryside so I decided that I would walk the few miles from Brookbridge station to the home of my great friend Arthur Van Houghton, the famous opera tenor and popular siffleur, who I was going to see. I had never been to the area before but he'd told me it was a pleasant stroll from the station to Rotherborough High Street, where we were to meet.

This was in the days long before smartphones and digital maps, and Arthur had told me to get out at the station and walk past the Wheatsheaf pub and then along the bridleway that travels straight as an arrow through the pretty fields and woods towards Martinsbrook. I was to go as far as the fingerpost at the crossroads in the little village of Brookstead Heath. The signpost, he said, would point me in the direction of Rotherborough, once the hometown of the celebrated aviatrix Betty la Roche. Arthur was to meet me at the top of the high street, under the bronze sculpture of the famous airwoman.

The train journey was uneventful and I got out at the station, and set off as instructed. There were many indications of hurricane damage in the dappled autumn sunshine, but much of the fallen wood and bits of demolished fence had been tidied into piles.

It was indeed a lovely walk and I finally reached the crossroads where the signpost was. And that's where the trouble started.

The sign was a charming black and white fingerpost of the old style, with four 'fingers' pointing from its central pillar. The problem was that the hurricane had blown the sign down and it was lying flat on the grass. I looked at it lying there uselessly for a moment, wondering what to do.

One of the signpost's fingers pointed to Martinsbrook and Coppesfield, a second, at right angles to that one and stuck in the mud, pointed to High Woodhurst and Rotherborough (my destination), a third, pointing in the opposite direction to the one to Coppesfield, pointed to Brookbridge, and a fourth, opposite the Rotherborough one, pointed to Buxfield Cross, a place I'd never heard of.

And then a thought struck me. I realised that I could easily discover which way I needed to go by using the sign, even as it lay there on the ground.

The problem

How did I discover from the blown-down signpost the proper direction to take in order to reach my destination?

Solution on page 185.

THE KNIGHTSBRIDGE BARBER

The mystery

Nowadays, Knightsbridge is an exclusive shopping district in London, but it began as a little hamlet that extended into the parishes of Kensington and Chelsea. Its ancient name comes from the Knight's Bridge that once crossed over the River Westbourne, which still flows through the city, but now underground.

One of Knightsbridge's most celebrated residents was Raymond Bessone, Britain's first celebrity hairdresser. Born in

Soho in 1911, Bessone anglicised his name to the more palatable Peter Raymond, but was known to everybody as Mr Teasy-Weasy.

Mr Teasy-Weasy was always impeccably coiffed and turned out, swooshing around Mayfair in bow ties, buttonholes and an expensive overcoat, which he wore without putting his arms in the sleeves. His Italianate looks were enhanced by his pencil moustache, but undermined by his entirely fake French accent.

Building his business and developing an exclusive clientele over the years was second nature to Mr Teasy-Weasy. Mixing as he did with the most fashionable people, he was always popping up in the news. Once, in 1956, the blonde bombshell Diana Dors flew him to the States to shampoo her hair. This reportedly cost £2,500, about £59,000 in today's money.

Mr Teasy-Weasy was never short of an opinion. He claimed that women over the age of twenty should avoid wearing long hair because it was ageing. If he was interrupted while doing nothing he would announce, 'Madam! Can you not see that I am meditating?'

One of Mr Teasy-Weasy's most famous reported remarks concerned the backgrounds of those whose hair he was styling. He said, 'I would rather cut the hair of three Cockney women than that of one Yorkshirewoman.' This, as you might imagine, caused quite a stir among his northern clientele, of whom, admittedly, there weren't hundreds.

The problem

Why did Mr Teasy-Weasy say that he would rather cut the hair of three Cockney women than one Yorkshirewoman?

Solution on page 185.

THE FASTEST BEARD IN THE WORLD

The mystery

In 1963 Sean Horn was seventeen and living at home with his parents in the USA. He was a precocious child and had a particular knack for the church organ, which he had learned from his father, a sober black-suited minister, who was himself proficient on the instrument.

Sean was also precocious in the matter of facial hair. His beard had begun growing at the age of sixteen and would by now have been long and bushy if his parents had not insisted on him shaving it off. They refused to allow men with long hair or beards to enter the house, on old-fashioned 'moral' grounds that were a mystery to Sean's normal, Beatles-loving friends. 'When you are eighteen, My Son, and have come of age,' said his

mother one day, 'only then may you grow a beard. If you must.'
Sean was an obedient boy so he shaved his face every day without fail.

Sean's friend Olivia Carlson had invited him to her all-night
Christmas party on 18 December, in the centre of the city, so he
asked his parents' permission. They were already trying their
best to accommodate themselves to the galloping changes
taking place in the USA at that time. Boys with long hair, girlfriends staying over, jeans, drugs, swearing and pop music all
seemed so alien to their world. But, though old-fashioned and
strict, they realised that their son was nearly a man so they
agreed that he could go to the party if he was back before
sunrise. He promised he would be. 'Make sure to shave before
you go, Son, and don't forget to take along a posy of flowers,'
said his mother.

On the night of the party, Sean put on his best clothes and
had a close shave. His parents approved. He waved them good-
bye as he jumped on the evening bus into town.

When he returned home just before the following sunrise his parents were astonished to see that he had a bushy black beard. They pulled it in disbelief but it didn't come off. It was a real beard.

The problem

Sean's hair grows at a normal rate. His beard is his own real hair, and there's nothing wrong with him. So how did he manage to grow a proper bushy black beard before sunrise?

Solution on page 186.

THE HIGH WINDOW

The mystery

The sloping walls at the foot of the newish-looking Leeds Combined Court Centre are no doubt designed to prevent people from standing around smoking or relieving themselves against the building. They add an extra element of charmless-ness to an edifice that, in its orange-brick brutalism, is already a bit short on good looks.

Not so long ago this was the scene of an interesting dispute, which sprang up during the trial of Mr Joe Slepkava, who was being tried for the crime of murder.

The story was that a man had been stabbed outside a pub overlooking the River Aire, which flows through Leeds city centre. Along the river's banks stand many renovated industrial buildings. Some are businesses, others hotels, and some are tall private dwellings. It was from a high window in one of these skinny 19th-century conversions that the witness for the

prosecution, structural engineer Marmaduke Snarbes, claimed
to have seen Slepkava arguing with the victim before stabbing
him and heaving him over the side into the water. Here is an
extract from the trial records.

MR CUMMING (PROSECUTION): 'Just tell us, Mr
    Snarbes, what it was you saw from the house in
    Chandler's Walk.'
MR SNARBES (PROSECUTION WITNESS): 'Well, I was
    in this small room at the top of number 69,
    inspecting it for my client. The main beam, which
    functions as a drag strut in the lateral-load-resisting
    system, seemed to have a problem with its acquired
    axial loading.'
CUMMING: 'Just tell us what you saw, thank you, Mr
    Snarbes.'
SNARBES: 'Oh yes, well it's an unused room on the
    third floor. Dark and dusty. Unfurnished ...'
CUMMING: 'Was it locked?'
SNARBES: 'No. It was jammed closed from outside with
    an old chair, under the handle. The wind whistles
    through any open doors up there. There is one very
    small square window in the room. It's got bars on it.
    No furniture, no chimney or anything in the room.
    Nothing – it's completely bare. Peeling wallpaper,
    bare floorboards, very dirty. Now, in the course of
    taking notes I heard raised voices, so I looked out of
    the window and I noticed a big fat man down beside
    the river. He had a spider web tattoo on his face. I
    saw him stab this other man in the chest and lift the
    body over the side, into the water. He threw the knife
    in afterwards.'
CUMMING: 'You say you got a good look at this man. If
    you see him in court today would you please point

him out to the jury? Thank you. For the record, the witness has pointed at Mr Slepkava.'

HIS HONOUR JUDGE QUATERMASS: 'You are certain, are you, that this is the man you saw?'

SNARBES: 'Yes Sir. The missing ear and the facial tattoo are distinctive.'

JUDGE QUATERMASS: 'Thank you.'

CUMMING: 'No more questions, Your Honour.'

JUDGE QUATERMASS: 'Ms Scrunt?'

MS SCRUNT (DEFENCE): 'Thank you, Your Honour. Mr Snarbes, you told the police when they took your statement that – now this is important – that you had seen this event by looking out of the window.'

SNARBES: 'That's right. I looked out of the window and saw that man stab the other one and push him in the river. I told the police that.'

SCRUNT: 'Mr Snarbes, you are a professional surveyor, a man used to dealing in numbers and space. How high is the window that you claim to have looked through?'

SNARBES: 'I didn't measure it.'

SCRUNT: 'Well, roughly – as well as you can remember.'

SNARBES: 'I should say, about ... I suppose about eight feet off the floor. It's a tall room and it's a small square window.'

SCRUNT: 'Eight feet? That is indeed a high window. It's about the height of a single-decker bus, isn't it? How tall are you, Mr Snarbes? In feet and inches if you prefer.'

SNARBES: 'I'm five feet ten.'

SCRUNT: 'Could you look over the top of a bus?'

SNARBES: 'No.'

SCRUNT: 'Yet you claim that you looked through a tiny, dirty window obstructed by bars, eight feet off the floor.'

SNARBES: 'Yes.'

SCRUNT: 'It's a smooth wall, isn't it? Or is there a projecting window sill or anything to grab hold of?'

SNARBES: 'Nothing to get hold of, no.'

SCRUNT: 'You didn't use rope of any sort?'

SNARBES: 'Rope? No, I didn't use rope or anything like that.'

SCRUNT: 'Mr Snarbes, we took pains to visit this room. It's exactly as you describe it, entirely empty and the window is almost eight feet off the floor. We took Mr Niblet, our solicitor, with us. Mr Niblet is six feet tall and plays basketball, and he couldn't see out of the window, even when he jumped up. And yet you say that you saw our client through this tiny aperture when you are only of modest height.'

SNARBES: 'Yes. Though I disagree that five feet ten is "modest".'

JUDGE QUATERMASS: 'Ms Scrunt, this is easily settled. We will adjourn, and you and Mr Cumming will take a couple of police officers and you will visit the room in question. Take Mr Snarbes too, please, and find out whether he, or anybody, can see through this high window in this completely empty room. You may report back after the adjournment.'

MS SCRUNT: 'Thank you, Your Honour.'

After the adjournment the court reconvened.

JUDGE QUATERMASS: 'Now Ms Scrunt, perhaps you can tell us: could you or the police officers, or *anyone*, see through the window in question?'

MS SCRUNT: 'Yes, we all did, thank you, Your Honour. I'd
    like now to move on to the badly blurred pictures
    from the CCTV camera on top of the Hungry Pussy
    nightclub ...'

———————————

The problem

How is it that Mr Snarbes, a man of normal height, was able to
see easily through a small window eight feet off the floor in an
entirely bare room? Even Ms Scrunt was able to see through
the window when she tried for a second time. Mr Snarbes
didn't use rope, wire, mirrors, a camera or any unusual aid.
How is this possible?

Solution on page 186.

THE CONFUSING COACH TRIP

The mystery

During the early part of the 20th century, when people had less
money to throw around than they do now, manufacturing firms,
especially in the industrial north of England, used to organise
works outings for their employees. They would send their grateful staff to seaside resorts or other out-of-town destinations to
blow the cotton fluff out of their hair and the coal dust out of
their lungs.

In the earliest days workers were ferried to Blackpool and
other exotic destinations in charabancs. The strange name of
these vehicles comes from the French *char-à-bancs*, meaning,
'carriage with seats', and your typical charabanc was an open-
topped horse-drawn contraption that over time gave way to the

modern motor coach, with two decks, toilets, tinted windows, air conditioning, entertainment facilities, vast luggage capacity and fat driver.

The first charabanc in Britain was presented to Queen Victoria by Louis Philippe of France and is today kept in the Royal Mews. Just the sort of present every queen needs. It is part of history now, and the word itself is seldom heard any more, though some older people still refer to modern coaches as 'charabancs'.

Works outings are a thing of the past too. Nowadays, tradesmen such as plumbers and painters seem quite flush with the old wonga, unfurling great curled wads of the stuff in the pub on a Saturday night, or flying off to Crete, Cuba and Thailand for what are now called 'breaks'. Many of them also seem to have second homes in Malaga or Florida, and zoom around town in flash cars and dark glasses, iPhones clapped to their ears. Am I straying into the land of caricature here?

Let's, for a moment, go back to the pre-motorised days of yore, when nobody had any money and life was simpler. Imagine that it is 1925 and you are driving a large charabanc carrying nineteen passengers from Birmingham New Street to St Ives pier. At their request, eight passengers are dropped off at Worcester, and two are picked up. Three get off between Cheltenham and Gloucester, where a peculiar foreign gentleman gets on with a harem of seven wives (each carrying several sacks containing cats and kittens). The resulting chaos prompts fifty per cent of the remaining passengers to leave the coach at Bristol, but five more pick it up at Weston-super-Mare, including two children, who travel at half price. At Taunton nobody gets off and nobody gets on. Then, at Exeter, one old man gets off and one old lady, with several bags of shopping, gets on but immediately gets off again. The journey then continues uninterrupted, with the coach arriving in St Ives on time many hours later.

The problem

How many brothers and sisters, if any, does the coach driver have?

Solution on page 186.

THE PILOT WHO WORE A DRESS

The mystery

Lufthansa is the largest airline in Europe. Its name comes from *Luft*, German for 'air', and *Hansa*, Latin for 'guild'.

Lufthansa is recognised as having one of the best psychological recruitment-screening programmes of any airline. Cadet pilots must go through a battery of searching psychological tests and interviews before they are allowed to begin their two-year training programme. The tests filter out more than 90 per cent of applicants, which is good to know. I wouldn't want to be flown by some fellow who had voices telling him to fly to Australia upside-down.

This psychological testing programme reminds me of the young man who was talking to his psychiatrist and said, 'When it's my time, I'd like to die suddenly and peacefully, at work, just like my dad. Not screaming and crying like his passengers in the back of his plane.'

Among the general queries about mood, family relationships, sleep patterns and alcohol use that airlines use in their psychological tests, I doubt that there is one that probes the trainee pilots on their sexual preferences. It doesn't seem relevant, does it? But maybe the larger airlines should take a leaf out of the book of some of the smaller outfits and include a question about transvestite yearnings.

One of the tinier airlines, Àcourt Dargent Air, based in the Crozet Islands, did, in fact, recently ask a trainee pilot what he would do if, after a long-haul flight, he met the captain wearing a dress in the hotel bar.

The problem

The trainee pilot gave an immediate, short, psychologically revealing, and confident answer to this query. It was exactly the kind of answer his questioners were hoping for. What was the nature of this answer?

Solution on page 186.

PICKING UP THE CHILDREN
FROM SCHOOL

The mystery

Suzanna Young lives in a modest flat in Croydon. On her mantelpiece she has a picture of herself in her wedding dress, looking pretty and, many people have noticed, rather sexy. It was her husband's favourite photo till he ran off with his secretary. Sue is a single parent now but she has come to terms with the idea.

Sue has two children, Mitzi and Sophie, who love her just as much now as they did before their father left them. They are identical twins, and always do things together, but from their earliest years their mum made sure to dress them in different clothes and treat them as individuals. In any case, although they look alike and are sometimes mistaken for each other, their personalities and attitudes are quite different.

Mitzi likes ponies, while Sophie loves sweets and netball. Mitzi has pictures of handsome film stars on her wall. Sophie has a picture of her mum.

Today Suzanna is picking up her children from St Juthwara's primary school. She is excited because they have been giving a talk about the Second World War (together, of course) to the assembled children in the school hall. Despite their confident personalities, the twins have been nervous for a couple of days. After all, addressing the whole school would be intimidating for anyone, and this is their first ever talk. Luckily their mum helped them with the preparation.

Sue arrives at the school gates and tries to chat to some of the other mums, but they have their own buggy-pushing clique, so she decides to wait in the car.

The doors open and the first out are Sue's children. They walk slowly to the car, they never run anywhere, and get in carefully. They tell their mum that their talk has been a great success.

As they are putting on their seatbelts, the school secretary runs across to the car, waving an envelope. She hands it through the window. 'Don't forget your fee,' she says. Sue's children open the envelope to find a £50 note. Something they were definitely not expecting.

Sue drives them home slowly. They all live together in the same block of flats, St Catharine's Court, but on separate floors and in separate flats. The fact that the block is a retirement home with stairlifts, assisted-living facilities, emergency alarm pulls and good wheelchair access doesn't worry them, and none of the very old people they meet remarks on their presence in a place purpose built for the elderly and infirm.

The problem

Why do Sue and her children live in an old people's home, and why do the people in the home not find it peculiar? They are not obliged to live there. Sue has plenty of money in the bank and they could afford to live anywhere else they chose.

Solution on page 187.

THE CAR IN THE RIVER

The mystery

One day in July, after weeks of rain, the rivers as the foot of Skiddaw in the Lake District were brimming. The Derwent, which rises at Styhead Tarn below Scafell Pike, England's highest peak, was flowing rapidly through the valley of Borrowdale and into Derwentwater. Its journey continued into broad Bassenthwaite Lake before it picked up more water from the stony River Greta, outside Keswick.

Returning home from a lunch near Keswick in his Land Rover Defender, Farmer Wynn Loss was driving through the magnificent Cumbrian scenery. The sun was high in the sky, the great horseshoe of Scafell Pike was away to his right, and, as he drove, he whistled happily to himself.

Reaching across to pick up his cigarette lighter, which had fallen from the seat onto the floor of the van, Wynn suddenly found himself spinning off the road and out of control. He smashed through a fence and began to tumble down a steep gorge before the Land Rover plunged into a fast-flowing river.

Wynn was suddenly alert. In slow motion he analysed the situation. The vehicle was in the river, and air bubbles were boiling up to the surface. He reached for the door handle but realised that he had broken his arm. It didn't hurt but a little spike of white bone stuck through his check shirt.

When he tried to unbuckle his seatbelt with his good arm he found that he couldn't do it. Neither could he operate the windows, which were closed except for a long thin one at the back which he knew was going to let in water, and through which he realised he could not escape. Before he had a chance to think of what else to do the car sank to the bottom of the river, with Wynn trapped inside.

For two hours the vehicle stood on the river bottom until, finally, a team of rescuers reached it. They found Wynn in the driving seat, still alive. He was complaining that his arm had really begun to hurt, and wondered what had taken them so long as his lunch had worn off and he was ready for his dinner.

They dragged him out, onto the bank, and a kindly soul took him off to hospital. A local garage volunteered to pull his car out.

The problem

Wynn had no artificial air supply in the car. How did he survive for two hours, strapped into his Land Rover at the bottom of the river?

Solution on page 187.

THE SAD END OF FELICITY FFOLKES

The mystery

Felicity Ffolkes had saved up for the holiday of a lifetime. She had always wanted to go on safari, and South Africa seemed a good bet: giraffes, elephants, zebras, leopards and, of course, lions. Felicity had always loved lions and hated to see them cooped up in a cement zoo in the wet city, pacing up and down like hospital outpatients waiting for their brain scan results. The sunlit expanse of the open savannah was, she felt, their proper home.

For her holiday Felicity settled on the Onvoldoende Game Reserve, a large safari destination, about the size of Israel. Onvoldoende has a full complement of wildlife, and the animals are accustomed to game-viewing vehicles driving up and down all day. This would mean a good chance of seeing the big cats that were her great love.

She was just getting over relationship failure number nine and would be going alone. She'd decided on the self-drive option through the reserve so that she wouldn't have to listen to loquacious guides talking about elephants not having scrotums, or sit next to sweating businessmen with tight shorts and porky polka-dot wives.

The time for her holiday arrived and, on the day, Felicity was finally ready. So, with factor-500 sunscreen and rubbishy holiday book safely packed in her luggage, Felicity took a malaria tablet and boarded her flight. It went without a hitch.

Once she'd arrived at the hotel, Felicity unpacked, put on her expensive new safari outfit, and popped down to the bar to show it off. There, a man with incredible creases in his trousers tried to buy her a drink. He was sent packing in a nimbus of aftershave.

Felicity polished off a couple of Martinis looking out across the pool into the shimmering blue distance. Then she hit the sack to catch up on her sleep before the next day's adventure.

She was greeted next morning by a magnificent sunrise, and after a light breakfast she got into her hired car, which was a new, expensively made, very solid German vehicle. It was a high-end model with doors so heavy they gave a satisfying *thwoomp* when you shut them. The electric windows worked well and there was excellent air conditioning so she'd decided against a sunroof. Felicity could photograph the lions with the windows up without any trouble. She checked she had plenty of water, and then set off.

The nearest entrance to the safari park was a mile away, under a swing barrier operated by a sleepy barefoot fellow in a floppy hat and dark glasses. He was smoking a funny-smelling cigarette and seemed rather too relaxed for Felicity's liking. He told her to follow the trail, not to get out of the vehicle, and not to open her doors or windows. He then waved her through and ambled back to his modest cabin.

It wasn't long before she saw half a dozen lions standing by a wizened tree. She stopped the car and took out her camera. As she started clicking, one of the lions sauntered towards her. It was a large male, with a handsome golden mane. This was great.

Felicity got some terrific close-ups as the big cat approached her. Her last picture was of the animal's open mouth as it gave an almighty roar. Thank goodness all the doors were shut and all the windows up. Then, with one swipe of its huge paw the lion pulled Felicity from the car and ate her.

They found her vehicle the next day. The doors were locked, the windows all up and nobody was inside. Some shredded safari clothes beside the car told the story. That was the sad end of Felicity Ffolkes, the woman who was eaten by a lion.

The problem

How did the lion manage to get hold of and eat Felicity while she was sitting in her well-made, new, hi-spec car, with all its windows up and all its doors firmly shut and locked?

Solution on page 187.

THE BLIND BEGGAR

The mystery

Nobody who has seen St Paul's Cathedral can forget the majesty of this towering masterpiece of English Gothic revival design. This lofty Anglican church is one of the finest and most interesting examples of early Victorian architecture in West Bengal.

Oh sorry, I should have said, I'm not talking about St Paul's Cathedral in London, I'm talking about St Paul's in Calcutta, now spelt 'Kolkata' by some rather touchy people.

St Paul's Calcutta is definitely a cathedral worth seeing. Its bishop, at the time of writing, is the deliciously named Rt Revd Ashoke Biswas, who sounds to me like a children's TV programme that I remember.

Calcutta is India's intellectual and cultural capital, bursting with eggheads and dapper gentlemen parading themselves through the cool parks and dreamy backwaters in fancy clothes, their poised wives decked out in the most sumptuous wafting saris.

Though these metropolitan types have plenty of money to spend, there are in the city many very poor people. Here and there barefoot beggars ply their trade. The classic outfit of loin-cloth, turban, scratchy beard and begging bowl is *de rigueur*.

When I was travelling in Calcutta as a young fellow I remember meeting a one-eyed Indian mystic who was performing tricks in the street. Mingling with the mendicants and market traders – his brothers-in-flim-flam – he was known, I learned, for Larraj, the little monkey he kept on a piece of string. The monkey held a jug into which passers-by dropped the occasional coin, as nearby pedestrians dodged the unruly traffic.

The performer, who spoke good English, told me his name was Mandeep, meaning 'Light of the mind', though once I got to know him he preferred to be called Max. I remember him showing me an eye-popping trick in which he used a wooden stick to move three wooden cups around on a mat. To my delight, small birds' eggs kept appearing and vanishing under one or another of these cups until, finally, he lifted all of them to reveal three tweeting yellow chicks.

I gave Mandeep a packet of Refreshers, which he found delicious, and he invited me back to his none-too-luxurious rooms, hoping, I suppose, for more sweets. As we sat chatting, drinking some white stuff he had made in his rickety kitchen, and discussing the unhappy condition of Calcutta's beggars, the mystic suddenly closed his solitary eye and posed a short but very tricky problem. This I now realise was the first lateral thinking mystery I had heard.

I racked my brains all night over curried goat and mishti doi but I couldn't work it out. When I looked for Mandeep the next day he had gone.

_____

The problem

A blind beggar's brother has died. How are the two related?
(They are not brothers.)

Solution on page 187.

A BIRTHDAY MESSAGE FROM THE QUEEN

The mystery

On 24 June 2015 retired bricklayer and family man Charles
Trimble reached his 100th year. He celebrated his birthday at a
small party with four generations of his family, in the retirement
home in Skegness, where he was then living. It took him ages to
blow out all the candles on his cake.

When Mr Trimble was born, George V was on the throne, and he has since lived under three kings and one queen, witnessed twenty-four premierships, and gone through two world wars, one wife and twelve fishing rods.

Thinking it would be nice if Mr Trimble received a celebratory greeting card from the Queen on his 100th birthday, Robert Nobbler, one of the nursing home's staff, applied to the official Anniversaries Office a few weeks before Charlie's birthday. He completed a standard form and sent along Charlie's birth certificate, as proof of his age. He received confirmation that his form and the birth certificate had been received in good time.

After a bit of a wait, Mr Nobbler got an official communication from the Anniversaries Officer explaining that, because of a technicality, the Queen would not be able to send Mr Trimble a birthday greeting until at least the following year.

Nobbler was beside himself with fury, knowing that there was no guarantee that Charlie would still be alive in a year's time. He rang the Anniversary Office and got through to a helpful person who calmed him down and explained the technicality to him. It was something of a shock to Nobbler and he was astonished to discover it. But when he went round to other members of staff to explain the point in question, nobody was surprised.

Anyway, Charles Trimble didn't get his greeting from the Queen in 2015, though his family were hoping against hope that he would still be around in 2016 to receive it.

Charlie wasn't bothered one way or the other. He was just pleased to discover that soft birthday sponge is the ideal foodstuff for a denture-wearer because you can eat it by taking your teeth out and just sucking.

_____

The problem

What was the technical reason which meant that the Queen was unable to send Charlie Trimble a greeting card for his 100th birthday in 2015?

Solution on page 188.

TALKING RUBBISH

The mystery

In the 1950s and 60s domestic households created far less rubbish than they do today. Our potato peelings, tea bags and eggshells went in the compost and any paper that wasn't torn into squares and hung on a string in the outside lavatory, or used to light the fire, was also put in the garden rubbish. Egg boxes were made of recyclable papier-mâché, not plastic, and housewives – remember them? – used to shop not by using a million plastic carriers but by throwing a string bag or a basket over their arm. Any greengroceries that were mud-covered or too wet to go into the reticule unwrapped were put into a brown paper bag, or rolled up in newspaper.

After a fish-and-chip supper or a curry, you didn't need a low loader to get rid of the polystyrene containers, plastic cutlery and plastic bags. There was much less packaging on supermarket products, too. Half a dozen sausages or a few slices of ham did not require ten minutes of cursing with a knife and scissors to remove the vacuum-shrunk casing.

If your tailor or outfitter sold you a shirt, he wrapped it in a bit of tissue and might have pinned it here and there. You didn't need to remove 1,000 mysterious plastic clips and acres of cardboard stiffeners.

If you ordered a cup of coffee you got a human-sized portion in a china cup and saucer, not a polystyrene bucket-load.

The morning after a party you were not left with an Everest of empty beer cans. You just had a few bottles that your friendly off-licence man would smilingly take back, before returning your deposit. Milk came in bottles that the milkman took away again every day, and the dustmen emptied one small dustbin per family per week, though they still managed to leave a trail behind them along the path. Nowadays, economy and make-do-and-mend have given way to so-called 'convenience' and instantaneous gratification. Just one skinny student now needs three huge wheelie-bins to dispose of just a week's mountainous garbage.

As a token of all this there is one particular household product, used today by nearly everybody in the developed world, which has indisputably made everyday life a bit easier and more pleasant, but at a tremendous cost. Every year, thousands of millions of these things are employed around the world. Although they could be reused, they very seldom are. Often, after being used just once, they are simply put in the bin without a second thought. They are therefore responsible for more sheer waste than any other household article on the planet.

This product is lightweight and extremely convenient, and, though it is now a part of nearly everybody's life, it first became widely available only in the 1980s. Since that time its careless use and disposal has increased at an alarming rate.

These very damaging commodities use enormous amounts of energy in their manufacture and, though small, they expand to many times their original size. They are difficult and expensive to recycle, so almost all are just thrown in the bin. Most end up in landfill sites, where it takes something like 300 years for them to degrade, about the same time as it takes for plastic carrier bags to disintegrate.

Over time they damage the environment by breaking down into toxic particles that contaminate soil and water, eventually entering the food chain. If they are carelessly disposed of, their massive surface area can easily lead to blocked drains, causing flooding and sewage overflows, and providing a ripe breeding ground for bacteria.

Ironically, these things could simply be wrapped up and safely tied inside a plastic bin liner before being thrown away. But this hardly ever happens.

The result of all this is that governments and consumers alike are under increasing pressure to think twice before they simply chuck these convenient but very harmful things in the bin.

The problem

What are these damaging items, which instead of being put carefully into a bin liner and disposed of responsibly, are carelessly thrown away, ending up filling landfill sites in their millions?

Solution on page 188.

THE FLOOD

The mystery

Most people know the story of the Flood as told in the Bible, but not everyone believes it. Modern research has suggested that there must have been about 35,000 species aboard the ark, and to a sceptical mind it seems impossible that a wooden boat of the size mentioned – about that of a modern aircraft carrier –

could actually have floated under all that weight. Indeed, since the 19th century scholars have agreed that the story cannot be literally true.

However, a recent study from Leicester University's Department of Physics and Astronomy has concluded that the dimensions given in the Bible would actually have allowed the ark to float even with all those animals on board.

Taking into account the size of the boat and the density of the water, scientists worked out its buoyancy force, which, according to Archimedes' principle, would be equal in weight to the volume of floodwater it displaced. They were then able to calculate the total mass the ark could support before it sank, and found that it would not have gone under. Whether it could have managed all that rain on top is another matter.

Here are edited highlights of the story as told in Genesis 7, from the King James Version of the Bible.

And the Lord said ... Come thou and all thy house into the ark; for thee have I seen righteous before me in this generation. Of every clean beast thou shalt take to thee by sevens, the male and his female: and of beasts that are not clean by two, the male and his female. Of fowls also of the air by sevens, the male and the female; to keep seed alive upon the face of all the earth. For yet seven days, and I will cause it to rain upon the earth forty days and forty nights; and every living substance that I have made will I destroy from off the face of the earth ...

And it came to pass after seven days, that the waters of the flood were upon the earth ... And the rain was upon the earth forty days and forty nights ... and the waters increased, and bare up the ark, and it was lift up above the earth ... And the waters prevailed, and were increased greatly upon the earth; and the ark went upon the face of the waters ... and all the high hills, that were under the whole heaven, were covered ... And the waters prevailed upon the earth an hundred and fifty days.

The problem

That's the original account from the Bible. It's a good story, even if you are unpersuaded of its literal truth. Now, here is the problem: how many animals, of both sexes, did Moses take on the ark? No going back and checking – that's cheating.

Solution on page 188.

HOSPITAL ASSAULT

The mystery

Wilfred Stansbeard couldn't get about on his own, and was in the specialist unit of a hospital somewhere in the United Kingdom. He was surrounded by a group of medical professionals, including specialist nurses, Mr Cutwell the surgeon and anaesthetist Dr Gasser, all highly trained and experienced.

The procedure he was in for can be life-threatening but is generally routine and safe. Once it had been done, it was expected that Wilfred would have to be specially fed and that he would be weak for many months. He would need to be washed and dressed and was unlikely to be up on his feet for a long time, though progress would probably be steady.

The time for the procedure arrived and it got under way in the usual fashion. It involved the use of a local anaesthetic, injected into the spine. The injection, though delicate, was accomplished successfully by Dr Gasser and all was proceeding normally. The patient was slightly dozy but conscious. Monitors bleeped. The patient's heartbeat was regular. Breathing and pulse were as expected. Voices were quiet and the progress of the procedure was monitored and recorded.

An incision was made and the operation continued to plan, but suddenly things began to happen very fast, the surgeon Mr Cutwell became intensely absorbed in what he was doing and called out for help; nurses moved swiftly, handing him implements. He was now giving authoritative instructions.

Then, before anyone knew what was happening, Mr Cutwell began repeatedly and deliberately hitting the defenceless Wilfred with his bare hands until he cried out in distress.

The nurses around seemed unconcerned at Mr Cutwell's attitude and a couple of them were smiling and chuckling as they watched this senior surgical professional with a wall full of awards and qualifications deliberately assault a person under his care.

Mr Cutwell declined to explain himself to the staff or to Wilfred at any time and, in fact, studiously avoided saying anything to him for the duration of his period in hospital, except on the day of his departure in a special bed, when he blew a loud raspberry at him.

This was not the first time this sort of thing had happened, either. This particular surgeon was responsible for many of these procedures and several times before had been seen hitting those he had a duty to look after.

The problem

Mr Cutwell was not an orthopaedic surgeon knocking bones about. How could he, a trained surgeon, treat a defenceless person this inhumane-looking way?

Solution on page 188.

THE TWO ITALIANS

The mystery

Recently, the painting 'Woman with a Yellow Dog' by Andrew Wyeth, which hangs in the Walker Art Center in Minneapolis, was revealed to be a fake by Italian forger Sofonisba Battista. Battista (1937–87) was an Italian who claimed to have forged more than 1,000 paintings by many different artists.

Born into a poor family in Milan, Battista taught himself to draw using home-made charcoal and paper scraps. In the fifties he made a small living restoring paintings for collectors but was also obliged to work as a dustman to make ends meet. He tried exhibiting his own paintings but they lacked all originality. Apart from a facile aptitude for painting in almost any style, his work was without any artistic merit and he found himself snubbed by the art market.

In revenge, Battista began to forge paintings by famous artists. These were snapped up by the same galleries who had disdained his original work, and he began making a lot of money.

By his third year as a forger he was grinding out paintings like sausages, often to match old frames that he had bought at auction. He said that even a bad forgery in the right frame would convince the so-called 'experts'.

Battista claimed that the Wallace Collection's 'Circe and Her Lovers', by Titian, the National Gallery's 'Blatchington Windmill in the Mist', by Constable, and the Pompidou Centre's 'Carrot Boxes' by Andy Warhol are all actually fakes by himself. In 1982 he suggested that the galleries X-ray the paintings, to reveal his signature in lead white below the surface paint. They all declined.

In 2015 a London auctioneer noticed that seventeen paintings by Salvador Dalí were on the market, all depicting an identical theme, 'Clocks Melting on a Staircase'. At the same time a schoolboy visiting a gallery showing one of these Dalí paintings pointed out that it was signed, very small but visibly, 'Sofonisba Battista'. It was the Emperor's New Clothes all over again.

Forger Battista confessed that the paintings were his and said he had included clues in all of them, the signature being only the most obvious. He told the press that he had produced the paintings as a protest against art dealers, 'who get rich at the artist's expense. They can't tell real from fake even when it's obvious,' he added. 'I'm hopeless at Dalí.'

To decide whether any or all of these paintings were by Dalí or, embarrassingly, by Battista, the London gallery called upon the services of two specialists in forgery, one a professor of

Chemistry, with a specialist expertise in pigment and canvas manufacture, the other a professor of Art History, with an encyclopaedic knowledge of the work of Dalí and five influential books on Surrealism to his name. Both taught at famous universities, both had stratospheric CVs, and both were Italians.

The two Italians turned up at the London gallery and, declining British coffee, were ushered into the back rooms where the conservators do their business. After a quick look at the picture in question, the Italians decided to roll up their sleeves and knuckle down.

Taking their bags, they went into the changing room, which had a coat rack, a bench and a few lockers. They removed their street clothes, bantering with each other, as men do in a locker room.

The strange thing was that although one of the Italian experts was wearing beneath his suit a normal outfit of boxer shorts and undershirt, the other was wearing a woman's bra (white and cream), frilly panties (white), stockings (stocking coloured) and suspender belt (white).

This was the first time that the two had met together in this way, yet neither remarked on the discrepancy in their clothing, and neither seemed remotely embarrassed by it.

Anyway, they got dressed, and cracked on with their work.

———————

The problem

Why should an Italian professor, who is not a transvestite, wear an outfit of very obvious women's lingerie, and not be embarrassed to change in front of an academic colleague with whom he has never worked before? And why is this man not surprised to see it?

Solution on page 189.

HOUSE PAINTING MADE SIMPLE

The mystery

Frank Copper Sr runs a successful domestic building firm on the south coast of England. He works with a team of associate craftsmen: plumbers, joiners, bricklayers and electricians. Frank also works with his son, Frank Copper Jr, who will be taking over the firm in due course, when his dad retires to concentrate on zooming around on his motorbike.

The Coppers' own houses take quite a bashing from the seaside weather, what with the salty winds blowing in straight off the English Channel, so they maintain their properties religiously and paint them regularly. And, of course, they are experts, so they get the job done efficiently.

Frank Jr's house was painted last year, so this time it's the turn of Frank Sr's house to get a facelift. The trouble is that they are so busy looking after other people's houses that they have little time to do their own.

Despite their hectic schedule, Frank Sr decides that, if they work together solidly over one weekend, they will have just enough time to prepare and paint two exterior walls of his house. The following weekend they can paint the two remaining outside walls, including drainpipes and woodwork, so that at the end of a fortnight all four exterior walls of the house will have been done.

But Frank Jr has a better idea. He suggests that they should paint just one side of the house. Frank Sr is bemused. 'But won't that leave three walls unpainted?' he asks.

'Oh, don't worry about that,' says Junior. 'Just you wait and see.'

Frank Sr decides that if he is going to pass on the business to his son he had better be prepared to accept some of his radical ideas, even if they sound incredible. 'Well, OK, let's try it,' he says. 'But if it all goes wrong we'll do it the old-fashioned way.' Frank Jr agrees, and his father notices an enigmatic twinkle in his eye.

The weekend comes. The weather is fine and the two Franks are looking forward to polishing off the job using Junior's novel scheme.

They first prepare one side of the house, rubbing down woodwork, filling cracks and gaps, and fixing up this and that. It takes about a day, but they finish at 5 p.m. and are able to enjoy dinner out at a favourite curry restaurant.

On Sunday they start early and by the end of the day they are halfway through the job, just as Frank Jr predicted. Things are looking good, though everyone Frank Sr tells about the idea is puzzled. How can they get the work finished by next Sunday if they continue to paint just one side of the house?

The following weekend, the two Franks work like stink, and complete the job on the dot, on their own and with no help, rinsing the last brush at 5.30.

They stand back to survey their work. Set against the rising slope of the South Downs National Park the house looks a picture. The golden summer sunlight casts long shadows across the lawn and various neighbours stop to lean on the wall and compliment Frank Sr on a job very well done.

The publican of The Neptune is having an evening off from behind the bar and he stops for a chat. He looks at the front of the house and admires the quality of the job. 'Smashing!' he says. 'It looks dandy.'

'You'll never believe it,' says Frank Sr, 'but even though the work looks complete from here, we've actually only painted one side of the house. It was Junior's idea.'

The publican looks at him in disbelief. 'I'm impressed,' he says. 'I can see young Frank is going to go far.' And he is right.

The problem

Frank Sr and Frank Jr have painted only one side of Frank Sr's house yet they've completed the whole job and Frank Sr is very happy with it. Nobody else has painted any of the house, but each and every wall looks as good as new, as if it has been freshly painted, which it has been. How is this possible?

Solution on page 189.

THE ABSENT-MINDED TAXI DRIVER

The mystery

The first London taxi service was provided in the early 17th century by so-called 'hackney carriages', horse-drawn vehicles numbering fewer than fifty in the early years. The derivation of the curious name 'hackney carriage' is lost in the London fogs of history, but may come from the village of Hackney, which is now a well-known part of the city.

In the early 19th century cabriolets (cabs) replaced the heavier hackney carriages, and the first petrol-powered taxis appeared in 1903, with meters being introduced four years later to work out the proper fare. Nowadays, the licensed black cab is famous around the world as the best taxi service anywhere.

Black cabs are firmly regulated. The licensing body is the Public Carriage Office, and it awards licences only to those who have completed a gruelling test known as 'The Knowledge of London', or just 'The Knowledge'.

The Knowledge was introduced in 1865 and it has hardly changed since. It is a long and thoroughgoing process of self-education, during which the trainee cab driver must drive around on a motor scooter, learning London inside out. A cabbie once told me that doing The Knowledge was like studying for two degrees at the same time.

A London taxi driver must be able to decide immediately the most direct route to anywhere, without consulting a map. The Knowledge therefore involves memorising some 25,000 streets within a six-mile radius of Charing Cross, such that the taxi driver knows the most efficient route to follow, without having to think.

It takes about three years to do The Knowledge, and successful cabbies take a pride in their familiarity with the entire capital. They have a magnetic brain for geographic information and will probably be able to take you from the headquarters of the Magic Circle to Vincent Van Gogh's London House in SW9 without you having to give them either address.

But this doesn't mean they never make mistakes.

One day, not so long ago, a policeman was standing in Albemarle Street, in Mayfair, near London's Green Park. Albemarle Street is famous for a number of things. The well-known Brown's Hotel is here, for example, as is the Albemarle Club, where in 1895 the Marquess of Queensberry left a calling card for Oscar Wilde, who he believed was corrupting his son. He famously scribbled on the back of the card, 'For Oscar Wilde, posing somdomite' (*sic*). This resulted in Wilde's unsuccessful libel action and criminal prosecution, the court finding that Queensberry's illiterate allegation was 'true in substance and in fact'.

Albemarle Street is also one-way. In fact it was London's first ever one-way street. So it was ironic that the police officer in Albemarle Street that day should see a taxi driver clearly going the wrong way down this famously one-way thoroughfare, against the flow of traffic. The cab driver, who was smoking a cigarette and staring into his mobile phone, seemed oblivious.

The policeman, who you might think ought to have known better, merely smiled as he passed, and did not try to stop him.

———————

The problem

Why did the policeman take no action against the taxi driver who was going the wrong way down a one-way street? He didn't know him, or owe him anything, there was no change to the one-way rule on the street, and he was particularly hot on penalising drivers disobeying the law.

Solution on page 189.

PLANE CRASH IN NO MAN'S LAND

The mystery

'No man's land' is the name for disputed territory between two opposing lines of enemy trenches. The term goes back to 1320, when it was spelled *nonesmanneslond*. Nowadays 'no man's land' is mainly used to refer to any area of unoccupied land between the opposing sides during the First World War. No man's lands (if that's the right plural) were often snarled with barbed wire and sprinkled with gigantic land mines and corpses, and no soldier from either side was keen to enter for fear of a whiz-bang taking his noddle off.

Because of the long stalemates, in which neither side was able to move forward without risking thousands of casualties, it was during the First World War that aircraft began to be used in combat for the first time. Large biplanes containing a pilot and an observer were able to plot enemy positions from the air. Bombers could then target their supply bases behind the lines.

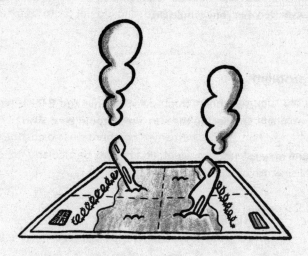

It was little more than a decade since the Wright brothers had made the first powered flight, so the new military planes were large and slow, making them easy targets for fighter aircraft. There were countless crashes and deaths on both sides, though many fewer than if soldiers had tried to cross no man's land on foot in the teeth of enemy fire.

Perhaps the most notable of these plane crashes occurred on the Western Front in November 1917, when five German Albatros D.IIIs came down in no man's land, along with two British aircraft.

Except for one German pilot and one British pilot, everyone was killed. The crash site was close enough to the British trenches for stretcher-bearers to bring back the bodies and the two injured men were immediately attended to by the orderlies of the Royal Army Medical Corps.

As some of the dead were German and others British there was an argument about the proper site for burial. It was decided that no man's land was not a fit place to inter the dead, so a

German chaplain and a British chaplain met to decide between them exactly what they would do.

———————

The problem

Once the sick had been treated, where did the British and German chaplains decide the survivors should be buried?

Solution on page 189.

THE STRANGE STORY OF ANTONY AND CLEOPATRA

The mystery

Shimmering in the heat of the noonday sun, the Great Pyramids of Ancient Egypt are a truly awe-inspiring sight and even the birds circling high in the wrinkled air do not reach their summit.

The pyramids are the work of the Old Kingdom society that dominated the Nile Valley after 3000 BCE. The most majestic, the Great Pyramid of Giza, is the only one of the Seven Wonders of the Ancient World still intact.

The Ancient Egyptians built the pyramids in just 85 years, between 2589 and 2504 BCE. During their lifetimes these man-made mountains have watched over plague, famine, glory and disaster. Once, long, long ago, they were silent witnesses to a mysterious double death.

It is the year 30 BCE, and, under the scorching August sky, the dead bodies of Antony and Cleopatra have been found lying together on the tile floor of a smart Egyptian dwelling that stands in the shadow of the pyramids. Both bodies are soaking wet, as is the floor.

There is no blood to be seen, there are no visible wounds on the bodies, and there are no obvious weapons nearby, although on the ground next to the deceased are several pieces of clear glass that look like large shards of a smashed round bowl. There is no blood on the glass.

Both Antony and Cleopatra have their eyes open and both are without clothes, shoes or jewellery. In fact, there are no clothes in the house except those of the owner. There are no signs of a struggle.

The owner is a rich trader, an animal lover with many pets including a boisterous dog that he keeps at home during the day to guard the property. Despite chewing the furniture and breaking the occasional vase, the dog never takes food from the table and is a good guard dog. But in spite of the double death he has not barked once.

_____

The problem

Antony and Cleopatra have not been poisoned, nor have they committed suicide, and neither have the bodies been moved. So how did they die?

Solution on page 189.

BIRD STRIKE

The mystery

If someone presented you with the flight record of Captain Ruby Darling, you'd be impressed by the almost unblemished history of this successful and experienced airline pilot.

Ruby began her career in 1999, piloting domestic flights around the UK. She then moved on to European trips before finally achieving her ambition of flying jumbo jets out of London Heathrow to various cities across the USA.

Being one of relatively few female pilots, there were initially years of friendly teasing for Ruby to deal with, together with a certain amount of blunt sexism, sometimes from colleagues but more often from unkind or ill-informed passengers. But by building up more and more experience Ruby's confidence also increased and she developed good methods for handling all this. Her husband, Trevor, who says his drinking buddies call him 'the captain's wife', claims that for every ten flights another anti-sexist comeback was added to Ruby's list of funny ripostes.

Over her decade-long international career, more than one airline has benefited from Ruby's skill and experience. Flying for two main companies, she quickly built up a reputation for capability and calmness under pressure. Her 2013 tally for successfully captaining flights across the Atlantic was 1,729. This is an interesting number, being the smallest number expressible as the sum of two cubes in two different ways.

Most of Ruby's early flights proved happy but uneventful, though once, in 2008, as she was coming in during a bad squall over Dallas, her bumpy landing slightly damaged the undercarriage.

The most serious incident occurred in 2013, when the plane she was captaining was struck by birds just as it was taking off from JFK airport, in New York. The incident report, which complimented Ruby's expertise, also noted the unfortunate death of the captain, who suffered a fatal heart attack. Luckily, though, nobody else was harmed.

In fact, Ruby dealt with the bird strike exactly as she was supposed to. As they were ascending, she saw a small flock of gulls rise up from nowhere and hit her starboard (right) engine. All her training clicked in and she made a brief call to air traffic control: 'Bird strike. Coming back.' She had lost power in the engine but managed to turn the plane successfully and bring it back to the airport.

Unfortunately, something went wrong as she was coming in and the landing wheel partially collapsed. There were sparks and screeches and a few bumped heads, but the cabin crew remember evacuating all the passengers successfully, in a perfect operation of its kind.

Ruby's husband Trevor ruefully laughs that, out of superstition, their children no longer feed the birds in the garden.

———————————

The problem

Ruby had flown 1,729 flights. On precisely which flight did the bird strike accident happen to her?

Solution on page 190.

CONTRADICTIO IN ADJECTO

The mystery

In Charles Dickens's *Oliver Twist*, Mr Brownlow is discussing the niceties of the law with Mr Bumble: 'You were present on the occasion of the destruction of these trinkets, and, indeed, are the more guilty of the two, in the eye of the law; for the law supposes that your wife acts under your direction.'

'If the law supposes that,' said Mr Bumble, squeezing his hat emphatically in both hands, 'the law is an ass – a idiot.'

Along with estate agents and bankers, the law and lawyers still have a bad name today, and there are many lawyer jokes, like the one about the man who asks his solicitor what his fee rate is. The solicitor tells him he charges £200 to answer three questions. 'Isn't that rather expensive?' asks the man. 'Yes,' says the solicitor. 'Now what was your third question?'

A friend of mine recently had to ring up one of these solicitor firms to get them to advise him on a vital but obscure point of English law. He finally got through to a partner, who he was told could deal with his query.

'Good morning,' said a voice down the phone. 'What can I do for you, sir?'

My friend explained that he had a question about marital law, a question that, until it was answered, would continue to cause his family tension and doubt. 'The question is this,' he said: 'Is it legal in English law for a man to marry his widow's sister?'

The solicitor gave him an immediate answer and said that his secretary would, in due course, be submitting notice of his fee. 'How much?' asked my friend, expecting the worst. 'Well,' replied the solicitor, 'it's £260.00 for my time, £22.00 for the phone call and £12.50 for receptionist services, putting you through. Then there's the preparation of my bill – that's £50.00 for typist services – £25.00 for my verbal estimate just now, and an amount for the letter setting out our discussion of this morning, which will be another £30.00 or so in secretarial time, depending on just how long is spent on it. So that's £399.50.'

'*How much*?', expostulated my friend.

'Plus VAT,' said the solicitor.

'In that case I've got another question for you,' said my friend: 'If you were a goose, what would you be able to do that a duck can't do that a solicitor doesn't want to do?'

'What a delightful riddle,' replied the solicitor. 'I have no idea.'

'Stick your bill up your arse!' said my friend, wittily slamming down the phone.

The problem

What answer did the solicitor give to the question about whether it's legal in English law for a man to marry his widow's sister?

Solution on page 190.

UNCONSCIOUS SEXISM

The mystery

Petworth House in West Sussex is a grand stately home housing paintings by Turner and intricate curlicued carvings by Grinling Gibbons. Its lush rolling grounds, designed by Capability Brown, are home to the largest herd of fallow deer in England.

Mentioned in the Domesday Book, Petworth stands at the junction of the east–west Heathfield-to-Winchester road and the coast road that takes drivers from Milford to the pretty bustling town of Shoreham-by-Sea.

But it is a stretch of the A285 between Petworth and the cathedral city of Chichester that has caused the town to be most frequently mentioned in the newspapers. In 2014 this length of road was officially recognised as the most persistently dangerous in Britain.

It was on an overcast, drizzly afternoon one November that a young woman driver, who had borrowed her husband's black BMW, was seen by portly, greying, middle-aged police officer Chris O'Brien, speeding dangerously along this stretch of road.

O'Brien set off in pursuit, aware that the woman was not the only motorist breaking the speed limit. Many men drivers were also going much too fast, some even overtaking the traffic officer's motorbike, which was itself going at speeds above 90 mph. But O'Brien decided that the woman driver was the right target.

For miles the woman zoomed along, spray flying, apparently oblivious to the police motorcycle behind her, but after some time, with blue light flashing and siren blaring, the officer, who was by now pretty grumpy, finally got the woman to pull over, which she did in an ungainly, some might say typically female way, ending up with her hubcaps scraping noisily along the kerb.

The officer dismounted and walked purposefully towards the woman's car. But the driver was not in the mood to be questioned and, jumping out of her vehicle, she unleashed a tirade of invective, swearing at the astonished officer in an eloquent stream of old-fashioned short English words well known to every stevedore and football hooligan.

Dumbfounded by the woman's fury, O'Brien, who was standing in the roadway, still helmeted, could do little but wait for the lady's screaming and yelling to die down. The nature of her complaint appeared to be that she had only been stopped because she was a woman, that many other drivers were speeding, and that most of them were men. 'You are a sexist pig!' she shrieked, larding her cliché with juicy swear words.

The dignified police officer did nothing for a moment, then passed a scribbled note to the woman driver. Still breathing heavily, she read it closely, running her scarlet fingernail beneath the words. It said, 'You are wrong. I stopped you because you were speeding and I cannot stop everybody. You may think I am a sexist pig but I am not, and I can prove it.'

'OK, then,' said the woman snottily. 'Prove it!'

'I think I just have,' replied the officer.

At once the woman realised that she had been quite wrong and agreed to listen to a friendly warning, which some might say was rather less than she deserved.

The problem

Normally it would take a long discussion, with lawyers, to demonstrate that the police were not motivated by sexism in a particular case. How did the officer prove so quickly that the driver's accusation of sexism was false?

Solution on page 190.

THE SHORT WEEK

The mystery

In the days of the California Gold Rush it wasn't the gold diggers who became millionaires; it was the entrepreneurs in what today we would call the service industries: the people who sold pans and shovels, the saloon bar owners, the grocery store proprietors and the cathouse madams. A man called Levi Strauss even starting selling the forty-niners blue denim. I don't know what happened to his company.

The Midwest had its own gold towns too. Deadwood, in what was then Dakota Territory and is now South Dakota, began as a Wild West gold-panning city. Lawless and drunken, the place became notorious for the murder of gambler and gunman 'Wild Bill' Hickok. This is the story of that murder.

On the first night of a hot August in 1876 Jack 'Crooked Nose' McCall was drinking at the bar in Nuttal & Mann's saloon. He joined a poker game with 'Wild Bill' and was soon losing badly. His luck failed to improve during further games and by the end he had lost his shirt. Hickok offered McCall some money to buy breakfast and though he took it he felt insulted.

The next night Hickok was again playing poker in the saloon, sitting with his back to the door. McCall approached Hickok and, shouting 'Damn you! Take that!', shot him in the back of the head. Hickok's cards dropped to the table as he fell, revealing a pair of aces and a pair of eights. Since that day aces and eights has been known as 'Dead Man's Hand'.

McCall fled the saloon, jumping on to a horse which was not his own. The startled animal threw him off and he fled on foot but was soon found skulking in a local butcher's shop. For once in Deadwood justice was done – 'Crooked Nose' McCall was found guilty of murder and hanged.

The horse that threw the murderer, McCall, may well have belonged to a mysterious visitor to the town. His name was Elmer Nemo, and he had ridden into town on Friday and stayed three nights, before leaving on Friday.

The problem

How did Nemo, who stayed in the town on three consecutive nights, arrive on Friday and leave on Friday?

Solution on page 190.

THE MAN IN THE LIFT

The mystery

Gordon Gordon is a well-to-do man of 38, with a memorable name and a forgettable face. He works as an investment banker in a City firm, tucked away in a bland office in London's Canary Wharf.

At the weekends, when he can escape, Gordon likes to drive his flash car up to his country house near Broxbourne, in Hertfordshire, where he keeps his green Wellington boots and his Land Rover, which he's had souped up, painted a remarkable red colour, and adapted in other costly ways. Gordon entertains his friends by taking them clay-pigeon shooting or rolling around naked with them on the rug in front of his snapping log fire, depending on whether they are male friends or female ones.

In the country Gordon has a Labrador called Stan and a beagle called Ollie. They are looked after by Mrs Johns, who lives nearby, because most of the time he is at work in London, crawling home late and tired to his so-called 'crash-pad', a small but comfortable studio flat in London's fashionable and pricey Docklands neighbourhood.

Gordon always turns himself out well. He has the latest phone, suit, shoes, spectacles and other things that he thinks matter. He is polite, charming and a good fee-earner, and expects to be a partner in his firm one day.

Punctuality is another of Gordon Gordon's strengths. He gets up at 5.30, brews up some strong Colombian coffee in his swish machine, and then does half an hour in the gym, which is along the corridor from his flat, on the tenth floor. When he moved into the block he tried to get a flat below the eighth floor, but this was the only one going.

After his shower, and a quick inspection of the state of his fast-disappearing hair, Gordon puts on his expensive suit, gets his stuff together, and locks his door. It's usual for him to be out of his flat by 6.45 so he never sees a neighbour.

He strolls along to the lift and gets in. It is a very reliable lift and never goes wrong. He travels down to the ground floor and walks along the River Thames to a little café he knows, where he has breakfast, and then over to his office in a building owned by a foreign financial conglomerate. He says hello to the ladies on reception, especially Monica, who has daughters taking exams and a soft spot for him. Then he travels up to the sixth floor where he works.

He is at his desk by 8.00 most days, and at the end of the day, which is often long, Gordon frequently takes a taxi home, though in traffic this can take longer than walking. But sitting idly in the back of a cab is one of the relaxing extravagances he allows himself.

When he gets into the lift on the ground floor of his apartment block he always travels only as far as the seventh floor, where he gets out, even though his flat is on the tenth floor. Despite often being exhausted after his very long days in the office, he always continues his journey by trudging up the last three floors to his flat, even if he is carrying heavy shopping, and even though he detests walking upstairs. The only time he makes an exception is if he is travelling with someone else, a friend or neighbour, say.

———————

The problem

Gordon Gordon is a man of intelligence and means, so why does he always travel all the way down in the lift in the morning but, when he comes home, get out at the seventh floor and walk up the last, exhausting three floors? He is obliged to do this for a reason that has nothing to do with the lift, the building, his thoughts or feelings, or other people.

Solution on page 191.

MARY'S MUM

The mystery

Mary's mum is a busy lady, juggling work and domestic life as a single parent. She has four children, all girls, and is eccentric in the way she has named them.

Her first daughter, now a successful businesswoman employing six men in her two bicycle shops, is called April. She likes scuba diving and riding. The second girl, a year younger than April, has just graduated from university and has landed a job at the Met Office as a junior weather forecaster. Her name is May. The third daughter, the prettiest, is called June. She is doing badly at school and spends most of her time staring into her smartphone. She wastes a lot of time on loutish boys and tells her exasperated mother that she wants a rich man to look after her. The final daughter has always enjoyed dressing up and putting on shows for the family. She is hoping to study drama at college. She likes modern jazz and makes a good pizza.

The problem

What is the name of the pizza-making youngest daughter, the fourth girl?

Solution on page 191.

THE DESERTED PRAIRIE CABIN

The mystery

Theodore 'Teddy' Roosevelt (1858–1919) was an author, explorer, soldier and taxidermist who, in a spare moment, decided to be the 26th President of the United States. He was what you would call a man's man. He loved the great outdoors, and, at his Elk Horn ranch on the banks of the Little Missouri, in North Dakota, he hunted wild animals and roped cattle, riding Western-style, with a cowboy hat on and possibly whooping.

On 14 October 1912 Roosevelt was kissing babies on the campaign trail in Milwaukee when he was shot by a disgruntled voter. The bullet was impeded by his metal glasses case, and the not un-long 50-page speech he had in his pocket. It made nice

holes in both before lodging in his chest. Refusing to go to hospital, Roosevelt delivered the speech. During the hour and a half this took him, blood gradually seeped into his shirt. You simply can't buy publicity like this.

Teddy Roosevelt recovered from the wound and it was another seven years before he died, anticlimactically, in his bed, from something else. It was said that Death had to take him in his sleep because if he'd been awake there would have been a fight.

Roosevelt had always loved the wide open prairies of the Great American Plains. 'We have taken into our language the word *prairie*,' he said, 'because when our backwoodsmen first reached the land and saw the great natural meadows of long grass … they knew not what to call them, and borrowed the term already in use among the French inhabitants.'

Beautiful in the summer, the prairies can be fearsome in winter. Blizzards howl across the great flat nothingness, blowing snow into huge mounds and tearing roofs off barns. A man who recently broke down in a snowstorm on the prairie decided to get out of his car and head for the light of a farm. They found him weeks later, frozen solid under a hillock of snow.

It was one day during the winter of 1889, close to the town of Bismarck on the broad plains of the newly established state of North Dakota, that a settler by the name of Hudson Flint found himself cut off from his farm by a sudden blizzard. Visibility was down to a few yards, but he was dressed thickly against the wind and his boots were stout. Somewhere nearby, he knew, was his prairie cabin, with a stove, fuel and dried foods. He must find it or he would soon leave his wife a widow. Time was not on his side.

Evening was coming on, it was getting dark, and the snow was fine and sharp. It stung as it speckled his face. Trudging through the knee-high drifts, Flint followed the line of a fence he knew well, having staked it out himself long before.

Finally, against the fading light of the swirling sky, he saw the familiar silhouette of the cabin. About the size of a garden shed, it was only yards away. Flint made it to the door, kicking the snow away from the entrance.

Inside, he clapped his arms around himself and knocked the snow from his boots. The room was as cold as the prairie outside, but, except for the thin blades of icy air that sliced between the slats, the wind was no more.

By now darkness had fallen and the cabin was pitch black. By touch alone, Flint found and gathered together an armful of firewood and kindling for the stove. Patting around the table in the darkness, he discovered a candle, an oil lamp and a matchbox containing a single match.

A ghastly idea now occurred to him. 'I have firewood, a candle and an oil lamp,' he thought, 'but only one match. If I cannot light the lamp, nobody will see my bright window and my fuel will run out before I am discovered. If I cannot light the candle I will not be able to relight the lamp if it blows out, which it usually does. If I cannot light the fire I'm as good as dead.'

The wind groaned and whistled around the chimney. Being a religious man, Hudson Flint fell on his knees and prayed for guidance.

_____

The problem

Flint has a candle, an oil lamp and some firewood, but only one match. Which should he light first?

Solution on page 191.

THE TWO PRIME MINISTERS

The mystery

When Thomas Carlyle got married, Samuel Butler remarked that, 'It was very good of God to let Carlyle and Mrs Carlyle marry each other, and so make two people unhappy instead of four.' Like Butler, Carlyle had a way with words. He called the hostilities of 1739–48 between Spain and Britain 'The War of Jenkins' Ear', because one Captain Robert Jenkins had said that a Spaniard had cut one of his off when their coastguards boarded his merchant ship. Jenkins' ear was later exhibited before the British Parliament and is supposed to have lit the fuse that launched the war.

The Prime Minister at the time of the War of Jenkins' Ear was Sir Robert Walpole, who is regarded as the first ever British Prime Minister, and also the longest serving. There is some debate about all this as the position of PM was never deliberately created, and didn't start on a particular date but evolved over time, like the nylon-eating bacterium. Walpole was in power for more than two decades and was enormously influential, but declined into ill health after he was accused of corruption, and of frequently going to bed with a woman who wasn't his wife. It sounds very much like the politics of today.

At the time of writing there have been 75 premierships in the UK, including some famous names such as the Duke of Wellington (who invented the boot), Earl Grey (who invented the tea) and Sir Robert Peel (who invented the police). There was Gladstone, Disraeli, Winston Churchill and Margaret Thatcher (who invented being the first woman PM), along with a few not so famous names, such as John Stuart, 3rd Earl of Bute, who was Prime Minister for less than a year.

The tallest Prime Minister is believed to have been Lord Salisbury, who was about six feet four. The most sexually fertile was without doubt Earl Grey, who had seventeen children. I take my hat off to him – it must have been all that tea.

Two lots of father and son have held the office, the first being George Grenville and his son William Grenville. The second lot were the Pitts: William Pitt the Elder and William Pitt the Younger. Pitt the Younger also had a family connection with William Grenville. They were cousins, their fathers being brothers-in-law.

The only brothers ever to have been Prime Minister were Henry Pelham and Thomas Pelham-Holles, who immediately succeeded him.

But the most interesting, and strangest, case among all these family relationships is the following. This is the matter of the man who was the 60th prime minister and the man who was the 62nd prime minister. Both these prime ministers had the same mother and father, but were not brothers.

Sort that one out.

The problem

If the 60th and 62nd British prime ministers (both male) were not adopted or fostered, and both had the same biological parents but were not brothers, how could this be?

Solution on page 191.

LOCKED ROOMS AND IMPOSSIBLE MURDERS

'The most beautiful thing we can experience is the mysterious. It is the source of all true art and science.'

Albert Einstein

THE TEA-LEAF

by Edgar Jepson and Robert Eustace

The mystery

Inventor and scientist Arthur Kelstern and iron engineer George Willoughton are firm enemies who, despite their mutual hatred, both make regular visits to a Turkish bath in Duke Street, in an exclusive area of London, where they scowl at each other through the steam, on the second and last Tuesday of the month.

One Tuesday in October Kelstern arrives at the baths at four, bringing with him as usual a thermos flask of China tea, which he likes to drink in the hottest room. Willoughton arrives shortly afterwards, joining his enemy in the same room, where the pair, who are alone, are overheard arguing loudly. Willoughton is heard to yell, 'Oh, shut up, you old fool! Or I'll make you!' In a foul temper he storms out of the hot room and goes into the shampooing room. A minute later a man enters the hot room where the pair have been arguing and discovers the body of Kelstern sprawled on a blood-soaked couch with a gaping

wound in his chest. Willoughton is promptly arrested but angrily protests that the crime is nothing to do with him.

The police decide that Kelstern has been stabbed while absorbed in drinking his tea. The flask is on the floor in front of him and some tea-leaves are lying in a puddle. Willoughton, they conclude, must have hidden his weapon under his towel, and brought it out of the room in the same way after the murder. But there is a problem: since coming from the hot room Willoughton has been in full sight of the shampooers and other bathers, who are all above suspicion. Despite searching, the police can find no weapon on Willoughton or anywhere in the Turkish bath, and neither is there any sign of blood on Willoughton or his towel.

Furthermore, the wound on Kelstern has been inflicted by a circular, pointed weapon nearly three-quarters of an inch in diameter, possibly something like an iron rod sharpened like a pencil. There is nowhere in the baths to hide such a weapon and, in any case, why would anyone planning to murder a man in a Turkish bath choose such a cumbersome thing when a hat-pin would have done just as well, and be hidden much more easily?

During the autopsy doctors concur with the police's supposition that Kelstern had been drinking his tea when he was stabbed: they find pieces of a tea-leaf, which has been driven into the wound by the missing weapon. They also, incidentally, discover signs of cancer in the old man.

Despite the lack of solid proof, the circumstantial evidence against Willoughton is overwhelming and it looks as though he will hang.

———————

The problem

How was Kelstern killed? Was Willoughton the murderer? If not, who was? Did the murder weapon really drive a tea-leaf into the death wound? And where on earth is this missing weapon?

Solution on page 192.

THE ADVENTURE OF
THE SPECKLED BAND
by Arthur Conan Doyle

The mystery

One day a young lady named Helen Stoner visits Sherlock Holmes at 221B Baker Street. She explains that she lives in Surrey with her stepfather, Dr Grimesby Roylott, in the crumbling family mansion. She says that Dr Roylott had married her widowed mother in India but that she died, so he returned to England with his stepdaughters, Helen herself and her sister Julia.

Miss Stoner's mother had bequeathed a large sum of money to Dr Roylott for as long as his stepdaughters lived with him. In the event of their marriage, however, each would receive a considerable annual income.

Two years ago Julia became engaged. Her stepfather offered no objection, but within a fortnight of the day fixed for the wedding her sister died in an extraordinary and horrible way.

On the night of her death, Julia came into Helen's bedroom. 'Have you ever heard anyone whistle in the dead of the night?' she asked. 'Because during the last few nights I have always, about three in the morning, heard a low, clear whistle.'

Helen suggested that it was the Gypsies whom her father allows to camp on the estate, and her sister went back to her room.

The wind was howling and Miss Stoner could not sleep. Suddenly, amid the gale, she heard the wild scream of a terrified woman, followed by a low whistle. Rushing into the corridor she saw Julia in her doorway, swaying to and fro in her night-dress like a drunkard. Then she fell to the ground, writhing in pain.

'Oh, my God! Helen!' she shrieked. 'It was the band! The speckled band!'

Hurrying from his room in his dressing gown, Dr Roylott reached his stepdaughter's side only in time to see her die.

Sherlock Holmes asks Miss Stoner what she makes of the reference to a 'speckled band'. She tells him that she believes it may refer to some band of people, perhaps the wandering Gypsies, who wear spotted handkerchiefs around their necks.

The coroner finds no evidence of violence or poison. At the time of her scream, Julia's door had been locked from inside, and the windows blocked by fastened shutters. There is no doubt that she was quite alone when she met her end.

Miss Stoner now explains that she herself has recently received a marriage proposal. Her stepfather has offered no opposition but some repairs have been started in her room, so she has had to move into the bedroom in which her sister died.

'Last night, as I lay awake,' she says, 'I suddenly heard in the silence of the night the low whistle which had been the herald of her own death.'

'These are very deep waters,' remarks Holmes, and he arranges to come to the family home directly.

Later that afternoon they arrive at the country house and Miss Stoner shows them round. Only one wing is inhabited and the bedrooms are on the ground floor, the first being Dr Roylott's, the middle that of Miss Stoner's late sister, and the third Helen's own. There is no communication between these bedrooms, but they all open onto the same corridor. The rooms' windows all look out onto the lawn. Dr Roylott keeps some animals from his time in India, including a cheetah, so the sisters' bedroom doors are always locked at night, and the window shutters are impenetrable.

Helen Stoner shows her visitors the room in which she now sleeps, and in which her sister met her end. Sherlock Holmes observes a bell-pull hanging beside the bed, with its tassel lying on the pillow. Miss Stoner says that it was installed a couple of years before, but that neither she nor her sister has ever used it. Holmes gives it a brisk tug. 'Why, it's a dummy,' he says. It is fastened to a hook just above a little ventilator in the wall. He remarks that it must have been a foolish builder who opened a ventilator into another room, when he might have communicated with the outside air. 'Dummy bell-ropes, and ventilators which do not ventilate!' he muses.

They enter Dr Grimesby Roylott's room. It is furnished with a camp bed, a plain chair and a large iron safe, which Miss Stoner says contains her father's business papers. 'There isn't a cat in it?' asks Holmes, lifting a small saucer of milk which is standing on top of it.

'No; we don't keep a cat,' says Miss Stoner.

'Well, a cheetah is just a big cat,' remarks Holmes, 'and yet a saucer of milk does not go very far in satisfying its wants.'

A small dog lash is hanging on one corner of the bed, tied into a loop at its end. Watson says it is a common enough lash, but does not know why it should be tied. 'That is not quite so common, is it?' says Holmes. 'Ah, me! It's a wicked world, and when a clever man turns his brains to crime it is the worst of all.'

Holmes tells Miss Stoner that Dr Watson and he will both spend the night in her room. They gaze at him in Victorian astonishment but he explains that when her stepfather comes back she must confine herself to her room, on pretence of a headache. Then, when he retires for the night, she is to open the shutters and put her lamp in the window as a signal, before withdrawing quietly to her old room. Watson and he will see the lamp from the village inn, where they are staying, and will come across and climb in through the window so they can investigate the cause of the whistle which has disturbed her.

That evening, from their room at the Crown, they see Dr Grimesby Roylott driving home, but Watson is puzzled by the whole affair.

'Well, there is at least a curious coincidence of dates,' says Holmes. 'A ventilator is made, a cord is hung, and a lady who sleeps in the bed dies. Did you observe anything very peculiar about that bed? It was clamped to the floor … It must always be in the same relative position to the ventilator and to the rope – or so we may call it, since it was clearly never meant for a bell-pull.'

'Holmes,' cries Dr Watson, 'I seem to see dimly what you are hinting at. We are only just in time to prevent some subtle and horrible crime.'

The hours pass slowly until finally they see Miss Stoner's signal. They cross the road and are soon inside the bedroom. Holmes whispers that they must sit without a light because Dr Roylott would see it through the ventilator.

He puts a long thin cane on the bed next to him. Beside it he lays a box of matches and a candle. He turns down the lamp, and they are left in darkness.

Suddenly there is a gleam of light up in the direction of the ventilator, and a gentle sound, like a small jet of steam escaping from a kettle. Holmes springs from the bed, strikes a match, and furiously lashes at the bell-pull.

'You see it, Watson? You see it?'

There is a low whistle. Then suddenly in the silence they hear a dreadful shriek. They enter Dr Roylott's room. On the table a lantern throws a brilliant light upon the iron safe, the door of which is ajar. On the wooden chair sits Dr Grimesby Roylott, clad in his dressing gown with the unusual lash across his lap. His eyes are fixed in a rigid stare and tightly bound around his brow is a peculiar yellow band, with brownish speckles.

'The band!' whispers Holmes. 'The speckled band!'

———————————

The problem

What is the speckled band and how is it implicated in the death of Julia Stoner? Is Dr Grimesby Roylott trying to murder his remaining stepdaughter, and if so how? What is the reason for the dummy bell-pull and the bed clamped to the floor? How did Dr Roylott die, and what was happening in that bedroom on the fateful night?

Solution on page 193.

THE GLASS COFFIN:
AN INSPECTOR JIBSON MYSTERY

by Anthony Butterworth

The mystery

One hot August evening Sir Herbert Hardcastle fails to respond to the dinner gong at his home, Bulstrode Manor. After a search of the grounds, his butler peers into Sir Herbert's large conservatory and sees the dead body of the 92-year-old man lying face-up on the coconut-matting floor. The door is locked from the inside and Meadows cannot get in, so he calls the police.

As soon as they arrive, Constable Ferry smashes a pane, pushes a hand through the hole, and turns the iron key from the inside to let people enter.

The conservatory is tidy, and, save for the damage caused by the policeman, not a pane of glass is broken. All the roof ventilators are tight shut, and leaning neatly against a banana plant is the pole that Sir Herbert used every evening to close the vents, which can be unlocked only from the inside by pushing them open or pulling them shut.

A small hammer is lying on a nearby glass table, along with a half-finished cup of tea. Ferry sees something in the liquid and, poking his pencil into the teacup, lifts out a blunt and rusty hook, about the size of a curled finger. It is coarsely broken off at the wider end. Meadows says that the hammer was used for smashing pots. He doesn't recognise the hook and wonders what it is doing in the old man's tea.

Inspector Jibson arrives. According to Meadows, Sir Herbert always finished in the conservatory at 5.20, before dressing for dinner, which he took alone. The housemaid reports that at about 5.20 she heard a loud bang, 'like a muffled shot or a door banging very loud'.

The pathologist removes the straw hat, which is still on Sir Herbert's head. He finds in the centre of the bald cranium a wound the size of a ten-penny piece. Sir Herbert has been struck once, hard, from directly above.

Meadows the butler points out that the pole used for opening the vents in the ceiling is, unusually, resting upside-down with its handle against the trunk of a banana tree and its business end on the coconut matting. He says Sir Herbert was most particular, and never left it upside-down: 'It always went back in its clip by the door once he'd shut the vents.'

Constable Ferry chips in: 'Maybe the murderer slunk up while the old man was looking at those flowers,' he says. 'Then he picked up the pole, walloped him on the head, and escaped across the lawn.'

'Brilliant!' exclaims Inspector Jibson. 'So our motiveless murderer picks up this long pole, and, visible through the glass from all parts of the estate, strikes an expert blow with its tip, in the middle of the man's head. Then he leans the pole against this plant, strolls across the lawn in the sunshine, climbs the fifteen-foot walls, dives noiselessly into the moat, and swims away. The dead Sir Herbert then helpfully gets up and locks the door after him.'

But if Sir Herbert locked the door from the inside with the murderer already in the conservatory, the man must still be in the room. A quick search is made but the murderer is nowhere to be seen.

If, on the other hand, *the murderer* locked the room, then he's escaped, goodness knows how, because apart from the ceiling ventilators, which are far too high to reach, there are no windows, and only one door, which was locked from the inside.

Inspector Jibson points out that the only person who could have been in the locked conservatory when Meadows first spotted the body was Sir Herbert Hardcastle himself.

'It must be suicide then,' says Constable Ferry. Inspector Jibson gives him a withering look.

'So he picks up this hammer, say, and bangs himself on the head hard enough to kill himself. Then he puts it back on the table, drops that broken hook thing into his tea, and lies down dead. Or do you mean that the hook fell out of the blue sky into his tea and he then hit himself with a great big window ventilator pole? I don't think that's even possible.'

A scenes-of-crime officer is examining the handle of the pole. There is a piece of straw stuck to the end, which matches Sir Herbert's straw hat. The tip has broken off the other end. He picks up the metal hook from the glass table and places it against the end of the pole. It fits.

'Pole leaning neatly against the plant but *upside-down*', he says. 'Hook busted off. Coconut matting. Of course! I see the answer. It's quite simple.'

_____

The problem

With such a wound, Sir Herbert cannot have committed suicide, but any murderer must have evaporated through the conservatory glass. So how was the old fellow killed in a room locked from the inside? And where is the weapon?

Why is the ventilator pole upside-down? What is significant about the coconut matting? And, finally, what is that rusty hook doing in Sir Herbert's tea?

Solution on page 194.

A GAME OF ROULETTE

by Sigismund Firthkettle

The mystery

My uncle Bob once told me that it is absolutely impossible to lick your own elbow. I don't know whether that's true, I've never tried, but one thing's for sure, there are some enigmas in this world so difficult to unwrap that you feel they are similar in difficulty to the elbow-licking problem. The following mysterious story by Sigismund Firthkettle is one of these puzzles.

As far as most people knew, Jim 'Smiler' Jackson was, before his failure to report for work, an unremarkable, 50-year-old employee of Fernsby Intaglio, a medium-sized security-printing firm near Cheltenham. The firm deals in tamper-proof labels and low-grade security-pass printing for a few government departments.

But Fernsby's is more than it appears. Since the Second World War the company has been doing a lot of highly secret government work. This work is handled by their so-called 'Shredding Section', and 'Smiler' Jackson was their 'Shredding Manager'.

But the picture is even more complex, because Jackson, a morose man who lived alone, is suspected by his bosses of treason. Intelligence from the nearby GCHQ has recently shown that he has been emailing secret photographs of the Yrdenob Desert nuclear reactor, along with names of certain Fernsby Intaglio employees, to an email address belonging to the government of the Republic of Apocrypha.

Fernsby Intaglio informs the police of Jackson's absence. They break into his house, which is locked and bolted on the inside, and discover his dead body lying on the sofa. On the table beside him are a glass of water and a box of supermarket aspirin. The packet contains a single plastic insert of eight pills, two of which have been popped out through the foil, and presumably taken. The other insert is absent, probably having been thrown away once empty.

The coroner asks for tests on the pills. It is known that Jackson was not allergic to aspirin; he was a frequent headache sufferer and often carried a packet in his pocket. When the tablets are analysed they are found to contain nothing suspicious. They are simply aspirin. The water is found to be just water.

A man comes forward to say that he recently met Jim Jackson in a local casino, where he was playing roulette. He says Jackson was flustered and told him he believed a person, whom he refused to name, was trying to kill him.

The coroner orders drug screening, but no narcotics, alcohol, sedatives, marijuana, cocaine or amphetamines are found in Jackson's blood, though there is a trace of aspirin, just the amount you'd get from one of the pills on the table.

His stomach is empty and the coroner suggests that he might have recently vomited. The signs are that he was feeling under the weather but, when it comes to it, the coroner has little to go on and is unable to decide what has killed him, so he records an open verdict.

But he has missed the true reason for Jim Jackson's death, which is that a long-planned murder plot by a secret government agent known as Bunce has finally come to fruition. Everything had been carefully set up. There was nothing to do but wait. Nobody needed to go anywhere near the victim, yet his death was certain to happen, and its cause would be undetectable. Its timing, however, has been impossible to predict, and its occurrence just as Jackson is starting to communicate with the hostile forces of the Apocryphans has been, for the security services, merely a happy accident.

The problem

Bunce has never met his victim and nobody else has done him violence. No one has broken into Jackson's house, and for some weeks he has cooked and eaten his meals alone. It is true that Bunce did sneak into Jackson's office on a hot summer's day six weeks ago but Jackson was not there. He was smoking a cigarette, outside in the sunshine, and Bunce was unable to see him. He left rapidly, being spotted by nobody.

So how has the killer Bunce done away with Jim 'Smiler' Jackson?

Solution on page 195.

THE TWO BOTTLES OF RELISH

by Lord Dunsany

The mystery

Smithers is a small-time travelling salesman who sells bottles of a relish called Num-numo for meats and savouries.

Looking for a flat in London he bumps into a young Oxford graduate named Linley, who is being shown round the same property. It is a nice flat but too expensive for either of them, so Smithers suggests that they become flatmates and go halves on the rent.

Smithers has an ulterior motive. He hopes to improve his sales technique by picking up some of Linley's 'Oxford manner'. He reckons you can make a quarter of an education go far, if you're careful with it. As he says, 'You don't have to quote the whole of the *Inferno* to show that you've read Milton.'

Linley agrees to the idea and they move in together.

Linley teaches him a little chess, which takes his mind off Num-numo in the evenings. Then one day Smithers reads about a ghastly murder in Unge. A man named Steeger has gone down to live with a girl in a bungalow on the North Downs, but she has disappeared. Scotland Yard is on the case but there is no sign of the girl and nothing definite to implicate Steeger in her disappearance, and, the police suspect, murder.

The Otherthorpe police have found out everything they can about Steeger, except what he has done with the girl. One thing which particularly attracts Smithers's attention to the case is that Steeger had bought two bottles of Num-numo relish.

He wonders why, with all Linley's knack in tackling chess problems, he doesn't have a go at the Otherthorpe mystery, which has knocked Scotland Yard endwise. Linley tells Smithers that he is uninterested in anything except chess problems. But he asks for the facts.

The girl was a pretty blonde called Nancy Elth who had £200 and had moved into the bungalow with Steeger for five days. After that she disappeared, and nobody ever saw her again. Steeger stayed in the bungalow for another fortnight, never leaving the place. When asked, he claimed that she has gone to South Africa, or South America, he's not sure which.

All the girl's money has disappeared from her bank account and, at the same time, Steeger seems to have come into £150.

Having watched Steeger night and day, the police have discovered nothing except that he is a vegetarian. They say that this is what made them suspect that there was something wrong about the man in the first place, for a vegetarian is something new to the local constabulary. They continue to watch him, but he has never left the bungalow since the girl's disappearance, and nobody has visited him.

They also know that when he came to the bungalow there were ten larch trees in the small garden, and from the time that

Nancy Elth must have died he began cutting them all down. Three times a day he went at it, for nearly a week, and when they were all down he cut them up into short logs and laid them in heaps.

These were the facts that Smithers gave Linley, along with the interesting information that Steeger had bought a chisel and a big butcher's knife. The police assume that he used these tools to chop up the girl, but they have found no blood on them.

There are some negative facts too. He hasn't buried the girl. None of the chalk under the bungalow or the garden has been disturbed. Neither has he burned her. He only has a fire in the small stove every now and then, and uses it only for cooking. There has never been any smell of flesh burning, just ordinary food.

Smithers asks Linley what he thinks has happened to the girl.

'Drains?' wonders Linley.

But no, the drains are clear. Nothing has gone down them – nothing that wasn't meant to, that is.

The body just doesn't seem to be anywhere. It isn't in South America, or South Africa either.

The police are stumped, Linley is stumped, and Smithers is stumped. And all the time the main clue, all that larchwood, is staring everybody in the face.

Smithers decides to visit Unge. He finds it a beautiful place to bring a girl to and he looks into the garden of the bungalow, where he sees the heaps of larch logs. He notices that the logs have been chopped roughly, any old way, and that the man who did it evidently didn't know much about chopping – it looks as though the axe was blunt.

Linley too cannot understand why Steeger should have spent so much time chopping all those logs, every day for a fortnight. If it hadn't been for a chance remark made by Smithers the mystery would have gone unsolved.

It is on the next day, when Smithers and Linley are sitting down to dinner and Linley is having a salad, that he asks Smithers to pass him some of his famous Num-numo to put on his salad. Smithers tells him, 'You don't take Num-numo with salad. Only for meat and savouries. That's on the bottle,' though he admits he has no idea what savouries are.

So Num-numo is no good for vegetables, then?

Linley goes quiet. After a moment he tells Smithers to call Scotland Yard to tell them they'll never find Nancy Elth. If they send a policeman round, Linley will tell him why.

———————

The problem

What has happened to Nancy Elth? Why did Steeger buy two bottles of Num-numo relish? And why did he spend two weeks of back-breaking work chopping up ten larch trees with a blunt axe?

Solution on page 196.

THE PROBLEM OF THOR BRIDGE

by Arthur Conan Doyle

The mystery

Ruthless American businessman Neil Gibson has settled with his Brazilian wife Maria and their two children in Thor Place, a grand old manor house in England. The Gibsons' children are being schooled by a beautiful young governess, Miss Grace Dunbar, with whom Gibson has fallen in love. His wife, who is described as 'past her prime', is bitterly jealous.

Late one night the body of Mrs Gibson is found on Thor

Bridge, a single broad span of stone over a shallow lake, half a mile from the house on the Gibsons' historic estate. She is clad in her dinner dress and shawl and has a bullet through her brain. No weapon is nearby but a revolver with one recently discharged chamber, and of a calibre matching the bullet, has been found hidden in the wardrobe of Miss Dunbar, the young governess. A note signed by Miss Dunbar making an appointment with Mrs Gibson at Thor Bridge has been found in the victim's hand.

Neil Gibson has asked Sherlock Holmes to help clear the name of his children's governess, whom he is convinced is innocent. Holmes has learned from a member of Gibson's staff that Mr Gibson was a man of violent temper, hated for the vicious way in which he treated his wife, who was much liked by the staff. Holmes is warned to be on his guard, because Gibson, who sleeps with a revolver under his pillow, is plausible and cunning.

Neil Gibson arrives at 221B Baker Street. He is a formidable character, and when Holmes asks his visitor whether he has been romantically attached to his children's governess he nearly loses his cool, but strongly denies anything of the sort. At this moment Holmes gives one of his famously airy replies, 'I am a rather busy man, Mr Gibson, and I have no time or taste for aimless conversations. I wish you good morning.'

Gibson is furious at the implication that he is lying, but finally sees that he must be absolutely truthful.

When the beautiful new governess arrived in his house, Gibson developed a passionate regard for her. He admits treating his wife very harshly and suggests that her 'crazy hatred' of the governess might have caused her to threaten Miss Dunbar with a gun that went off in a scuffle, fatally wounding Mrs Gibson. Holmes agrees that it is the only obvious alternative to deliberate murder by Miss Dunbar.

Holmes and Watson decide to visit Gibson's country estate, where a policeman shows them the spot on the bridge where

Mrs Gibson was discovered. Holmes is told that the deadly gunshot was fired from just behind the right temple. There was no trace of a struggle, and no weapon. The victim was lying on her back with the note from Miss Dunbar clutched in her left hand and it is clear that nobody could have put the paper in the victim's hand after her death. The note reads, 'I will be at Thor Bridge at nine o'clock. G. DUNBAR'.

Why, he wonders, was the lady still clasping the note in her hand? Why should she carry it so carefully?

With his famous lens Holmes inspects the opposite parapet of the bridge. There is a newly made white chip out of the grey stone, as if it has been struck a sharp blow. It has not been made from above but from below, and is on the lower edge of the parapet.

The stolid policeman points out that the mark is fifteen feet from where the body lay and Holmes agrees that it may be irrelevant.

Watson, as usual, is mystified by everything but Holmes points out that although the case looks black against the governess there is one point in her favour, which is the finding of the pistol in her wardrobe.

'We must look for consistency,' he says. 'Where there is a want of it we must suspect deception.'

Holmes goes over the actions of a woman who, in a cold, premeditated fashion, is about to get rid of a rival. She has planned it. A note has been written. The victim has come. She has her gun. The crime is done. It has been workmanlike and complete. Would so crafty a criminal carefully carry the weapon home and put it in her own wardrobe, the very first place that would be searched, when she might easily have flung it into the reed beds? Holmes believes that they are in the presence of 'a serious misconception'.

The governess disclaims knowledge of the gun, which she says is one of a pair belonging to Mr Gibson. By Holmes's new theory, she is speaking the truth. Therefore it must have been placed in her wardrobe by someone who wished to incriminate her.

'You see,' he says, 'how we come at once upon a most fruitful line of inquiry.'

Watson accompanies Holmes to interview Miss Dunbar in prison. She explains that on the day in question she received a note from Mrs Gibson imploring her to meet her as she had something important to tell her. She asked Miss Dunbar to burn the note and to leave an answer on the sundial in the garden, as she wanted nobody, including her husband, whom she greatly feared, to know that they were meeting.

The governess says she did as she was asked and in the evening went down to Thor Bridge as she had promised, where Mrs Gibson was waiting. 'She was like a mad woman … subtly mad with the deep power of deception which insane people may have,' says the governess.

Miss Dunbar explains that Mrs Gibson poured out her 'whole wild fury', and that she just put her hands over her ears and rushed back to her room.

Holmes raises the subject of the chip in the stonework of the bridge. Miss Dunbar cannot explain it but says that it must have been made with great violence. Holmes is suddenly overcome with excitement. He bundles Watson out of the jail, calling out to the bemused Miss Dunbar, 'With the help of the god of justice I will give you a case which will make England ring … take my assurance that the clouds are lifting and that I have every hope that the light of truth is breaking through.'

The problem

What exactly happened on Thor Bridge that night? Is Miss Dunbar guilty of murdering Mrs Gibson? How did the gun get

into her wardrobe? Is the violent Neil Gibson concealing something? Why was Mrs Gibson clasping Miss Dunbar's note in her
hand? What is the meaning of the mysterious chip in the
stonework on the bridge, and why should it have appeared at
the very time and place of the tragedy?

Solution on page 197.

LATERAL THINKING
MYSTERIES FROM REAL LIFE

'Every man at the bottom of his heart believes
that he is a born detective.'

John Buchan

ARSENIC AND OLD LUCE

The mystery

Clare Boothe Luce (1903–87), an American writer, editor, congresswoman and socialite, with a waspish tongue and an intriguing past, was born Ann Clare Boothe, the second illegitimate child of a dancer and a patent-medicine salesman. In 1935 Clare married Henry Luce, the publisher of *Time* and *Life*, whereupon an observer remarked that despite life's woes she had 'a knack for landing with her arse in the marmalade'.

In 1953 President Eisenhower made Clare Boothe Luce ambassador to Italy, but on her arrival in Rome she found that, as a forthright Republican anti-communist in a country with a strong Communist party, she wasn't exactly flavour of the month.

All the same she set to work, revamping her official residence, the Villa Taverna, a place famous for its fancy gardens and Renaissance interior.

She was clearly determined to have everything just the way she wanted it, and rearranged not only her apartment but her

staff too. Noticing the speed with which the new ambassador had given her press attaché the bum's rush, embassy staffers became anxious for their own jobs.

But nobody could deny her discipline. The ambassador began each day with an 8 o'clock breakfast in her room followed by a busy round of engagements, interrupted only by lunch. She was back in her rooms at 7 p.m. to dress for what was often more than one party, and was seldom in bed before midnight.

Famous for her acid tongue, the ambassador soon ruffled feathers by complaining about the washing machine in the busy laundry room above her. This had been rattling her awake every day at the crack of dawn. She was also upsetting the Italians with some undiplomatic comments. It looked as if she was determined to make enemies everywhere.

And it wasn't long before she started to feel strangely unwell. Chronic stomach upsets were putting her off the food prepared by her kitchen staff at the residence, and at the endless round of embassy dinners. She complained that her morning coffee tasted unnaturally bitter.

After she had been in the job for three months her husband Henry Luce paid a visit and was shocked by her gaunt figure. She was by now desperately fatigued and nauseous, and was starting to lose sensation in one of her legs, which she found she had to drag.

Taking a break in the US, Clare Boothe Luce began to feel better, but on returning to Rome her symptoms came back with a vengeance. Her fingernails were now breaking, her teeth becoming loose, and she was starting to behave weirdly at functions, complaining on one occasion of flying saucers on the roof.

Finally she went for tests at a US naval hospital and was advised to return to the States for Christmas. Over the holiday she received an urgent handwritten letter informing her that traces of arsenic had been discovered in one of her urine samples. The CIA explained that she had probably been receiving small doses over a long period.

It seemed that the ambassador was being regularly poisoned in Rome, possibly at the embassy or the residence, or at the functions she attended. Was someone putting something in her coffee?

Colourless and tasteless, arsenic is an ideal poison to administer in food or drink, and investigators realised that any poisoner must have access to the ambassador's meals.

She was told to stay in the US as a gigantic operation was set in motion to look into the political backgrounds of likely suspects inside and outside the embassy and residence. Agents disguised as workmen arrived to begin surreptitiously investigating the staff.

Chefs and servants were watched closely, but since Clare Boothe Luce was not there to be poisoned they drew a blank. In any event, no evidence was discovered that anyone was tampering with the ambassador's food.

Then one day in the private apartments an observant agent noticed a sprinkling of grey dust in Clare Boothe Luce's makeup and on one of the Linguaphone discs that she was using to learn Italian. On analysis the dust was found to contain minute amounts of poisonous lead arsenate ...

_____

The problem

How was Clare Boothe Luce being poisoned? Was there any truth in the rumour that extermination agents of the Soviet Union were trying to murder her? Or was something else going on here?

Solution on page 198.

THE RATHER-SHORT-VERY-LONG BASEBALL GAME

The mystery

Past President of The Explorers Club, Captain Alfred Scott McLaren, USN (Ret.), PhD, FE '71, is a graduate of the US Naval Academy and US Naval War College. He holds postgraduate degrees from George Washington University and Cambridge University. Captain McLaren has been on more than twenty Cold War missions and, to add to his list of illustrious awards, he's got the Distinguished Service Medal, two Legions of Merit and four Navy Unit Citations.

Before his retirement from the navy, Captain McLaren was a nuclear attack submarine officer and climate change research scientist. He is one of the few people to have dived to the *Titanic*, he has visited the deep wreck of the German battleship

Bismarck, and he's explored the hydrothermal vents that sit along the Mid-Atlantic Ridge, where chemicals dissolved in the vent fluids support complex communities of bacteria, giant tube worms, clams, limpets and shrimp.

I've just been reading Captain McLaren's fascinating book, *Silent and Unseen: On Patrol in Three Cold War Attack Submarines*, in which he describes one of his most exciting adventures, which happened on 25 August 1960, when the USS *Seadragon*, on which he was patrolling, broke the surface under an early-morning August sun. They were close to land that belonged to neither the US nor the USSR, but under international law both had exploration rights in the area.

The air was fresh and the sky blue, so a party was dispatched to set up camp on land, several hundred yards from the submarine. One of the crew's duties that morning was to undertake an exercise designed to test the speed at which they could evacuate the sub in an emergency, so they got down to the job in hand.

But all work and no play makes Jack a dull boy, so Captain McLaren and the other officers and crew of the *Seadragon* decided to have a game of baseball. In fact they had been talking about it for days in the confined quarters of the boat. Fresh air and outdoor exercise are in short supply on a submarine and, unlike tiddly-winks, baseball is not a recommended underwater pastime. The clear open land provided an inviting opportunity.

The game promised to be an exciting and possibly heated contest between engineers aft and those who worked forward of the *Seadragon*'s nuclear reactor compartment. But the match had hardly got under way when a player whacked a fly ball into right field, where a fielder caught it. Normally the batsman would have been out, but owing to a curiosity it was clear to everybody that he could not possibly be considered out for another 24 hours. They would either have to allow him to remain in or stop the game and sit around chatting for an interminable time to await the decision.

As if this wasn't odd enough, a player soon hit a ball into left field. There it was caught and thrown to first base, where again no decision could be made until the following day.

Action around second base was proving to be troublesome too. Everyone was running as fast as they could, throwing as hard and as accurately as they could, but every action was taking several days to complete.

The game continued like this until the end. Nobody could remember what day it was or how many days they had been playing when the game finally finished, and the umpire went mad trying to work out the scores.

The problem

All the players were fit and well, and the umpire was sound of body and mind. So what was it about this game of baseball that meant whole days were passing between shots being taken and decisions being made?

Solution on page 199.

THE CURIOUS CASE OF DIHYDROGEN MONOXIDE

The mystery

For years, campaigner Tom Way has been trying to alert the world to the dangers of dihydrogen monoxide, a deadly chemical compound that is used by industry in everything from spray-on oven cleaners to nuclear reactors. It is used as a fire-retardant and is an industrial solvent so corrosive that it can eat holes into solid metal. At root DHMO is a highly reactive hydroxyl radical that can mutate DNA, disrupt cell membranes and chemically alter vital neurotransmitters. Ingestion of the compound can cause painful abdominal bloating and diuresis, while accidental inhalation, even in small quantities, results in many deaths every year.

Dihydrogen monoxide has no detectible smell and is quite colourless, so its presence in household products easily goes unnoticed. It has been detected in varying amounts in liquid bubble products sold to children, as well as in jars of baby food, high-fat cakes and pies, and in the most popular brands of high-sugar and high-calorie soft drinks. Its frequent use in bath products and cosmetics is often concealed by use of alternative names.

The liquid, solid and gaseous forms of DHMO have all been a major contributory factor to serious air crashes, and in its gaseous form it causes severe burns to humans, especially children. Lengthy exposure to its solid form, though less common, leads to tissue necrosis, limb amputation and ultimately death.

Dihydrogen monoxide has been found in relatively large amounts in public swimming pools, where it is claimed to 'maintain chemical balance', and although it continues to result in numerous deaths, its use in pools is still not illegal.

While well aware of the dangers of dihydrogen monoxide, the UK government does not classify it as toxic or cancer causing, as it does with other dangerous compounds. It is worth remembering, however, that all governments are aware of the inconvenient truth that if its use were to be banned industry would grind to a halt.

Though most people have never heard of DHMO, when told about it overwhelming numbers surveyed in the US said that it should be banned.

Here is a short list of some of the dangers and questionable uses of dihydrogen monoxide:

- Dihydrogen monoxide is present in high concentrations in acid rain.
- Exposure to DHMO decreases the effectiveness of vehicle brakes and is the direct cause of many road accidents every year in the UK and abroad.
- Dihydrogen monoxide is deliberately put into the food given to banned pit bull terriers and other dangerous dogs.
- Though dihydrogen monoxide is consciously fed to prisoners in UK prisons, and also in Guantanamo Bay Detention Camp, it is deliberately not given that name.
- DHMO has been used to greatly heighten the effect of so-called 'waterboarding', which, without it, is much less effective.

_____

The problem

Pressure groups such as DHMO.org that fight to encourage the public to think carefully about this compound and its deliberately confusing names have had very little success. Why is something so harmful, corrosive and dangerous to humans almost universally used by industry without governments objecting?

Get your lateral thinking cap on.

Solution on page 200.

THE *MARY CELESTE* AFFAIR

The mystery

Of all the 'ghost ship' mysteries to have haunted the minds of sailors and landlubbers alike down the years, surely the strange case of the *Mary Celeste* is the most thrilling.

Mary Celeste was an American merchant brigantine, a kind of two-masted sailing ship, which was spotted adrift off the Azores on 4 December 1872, with her lifeboat missing and nobody aboard.

She had left New York for Genoa a month earlier, and was well stocked with provisions. The personal belongings of the captain and crew were undisturbed, as was the ship's cargo: 1,709 barrels of denatured alcohol (methylated spirits).

The *Los Angeles Times* later described the scene in dramatic detail: 'Every sail was set, the tiller was lashed fast, not a rope was out of place … The fire was burning in the galley. The dinner was standing untasted and scarcely cold.'

As is usual with newspapers, this account was full of inaccuracies. Every sail was *not* set, the tiller was *not* lashed, several ropes and bits of equipment *were* out of place, the fire was *not* burning in the galley, and *no* meal – cold or otherwise – was standing untasted in the galley, on the tables, or anywhere else.

The *Los Angeles Times* was not alone in its embellishments. Explanations included an attack by bloodthirsty pirates and, more recently, paranormal woo-woo of various sorts, including 'flying-saucer abduction' by aliens with funny eyes. *Chambers's Journal* went as far as to suggest that the crew of the *Mary Celeste* had been grabbed by the huge tentacles of a giant squid and eaten alive.

Twelve years after the event, in January 1884, the *Mary Celeste* story was retold in an issue of *The Cornhill Magazine*. This fictional account was by a 25-year-old ship's surgeon named Arthur Conan Doyle – it was one of his more successful early works. In his story Doyle renamed the ship *Marie Celeste*, and the name stuck, such that even today there is confusion over the vessel's proper appellation.

The true story was this. On Thursday 7 November 1872, *Mary Celeste* left the harbour of New York in fair weather, and sailed out into the Atlantic on her journey towards the metaphorical groin at the top of the great thigh-length boot of Italy. The weather was rough and the captain and crew had to deal with strong winds from the time they left New York until they arrived at Santa Maria Island, in the Azores, sailing the last stretch in a gale.

About a month later, at around 1 p.m. on Wednesday 4 December land time (5 December sea time), the helmsman of a ship named *Dei Gratia*, sailing far from land at a position about halfway between the Azores and Portugal, reported a vessel

drifting erratically, about six miles off. Her unsteady move-
ments and the odd set of her sails led the captain to suspect that
something was amiss. The ship was heading towards them and
as the two vessels approached each other the name on her side
gradually became clear. She was the *Mary Celeste*.

Signals were sent but none were replied to, and as she drew
closer it looked as though her deck had been abandoned.

The captain dispatched two men over the side to investigate
and the pair scrambled aboard.

They found the ship deserted. Much of the rigging was
damaged and ropes were dangling slack over the hull. The main
hatch cover was on tight but other hatches were open, their
covers sitting beside them on the deck. The sails were partly set
but were in a poor condition, with some of them absent alto-
gether. Galley equipment was neatly stowed but the ship's
compass housing had been damaged.

On the deck was a bilge valve and a rough-and-ready sounding rod, a tool used for measuring the depth of water in the hold,
of which there was a significant amount. The depth was meas-
ured by the search party at some 3.5 feet, but this was not an
unmanageable amount for a craft of the size of the *Mary Celeste*.

The crew seemed to have been taking readings in the hull,
possibly believing that the ship was taking on water much faster
than it was, and was going to sink. The open hatches, with their
covers off, suggest a hurried departure, possibly following an
inspection or a venting of the volatile cargo of alcohol. There
were no signs of fire.

Most significantly, the ship's only lifeboat was missing from
its position lashed to the cover of the main hatch. Cut marks
seemed to show that, instead of being untied, the ropes that
held it fast had been severed with an axe.

The ship's cabins were wet, water having come in through
open doorways and skylights, but they were tidy and in good
order. Personal items were scattered about the captain's cabin,

including a sword under the bed, but there was no evidence of a scuffle, or violence of any kind. However, the bed was unmade, something unusual aboard a well-run ship unless the captain had been roused from sleep at the time of an alarm. Most of the ship's papers, along with the captain's navigational instruments, were missing.

The ship's log was found in the mate's cabin. The final entry was timed at 8 a.m. on 25 November, nine days earlier. *Mary Celeste*'s last position was recorded as 37°01'N, 25°01'W, off Santa Maria Island in the Azores, nearly 400 nautical miles (about 460 land miles) from the place where *Dei Gratia* had come upon her.

The *Mary Celeste* was sailed directly into port, and hearings were begun in Gibraltar in December. These were conducted by the boisterously named Frederick Solly-Flood, Attorney General of Gibraltar and Proctor for the Queen in Her Office of Admiralty – a title which would require quite a big badge to fit on for Admiralty strategy conferences. Flood was by all accounts a man 'whose arrogance and pomposity were inversely proportional to his IQ', and he was convinced that a crime had been committed. He demanded to see evidence.

Almost at once, Gibraltar's Surveyor of Shipping, John Austin, found on the captain's sword traces of what appeared to be blood. Possible bloodstains were also discovered on one of the ship's rails, along with peculiar cuts on the hull. A report decided that the ship had not been in a collision or run aground, and Austin found these cuts highly suspicious. In his official report he remarked:

I found on the bow, between two and three feet above the water line on the port side, a long narrow strip at the edge of a plank under the cat-head cut away to the depth of about three eighths of an inch and about one and a quarter inches wide for a length of about six to seven feet. This injury had been sustained recently and could not have been effected by weather or collision and was apparently done by a sharp cutting instrument continuously applied through the whole length of the injury. I found on the starboard bow but a little further from the stern of the vessel a precisely similar injury at the edge of a plank but perhaps an eighth or tenth of an inch wider, which in my opinion had been effected simultaneously and by the same means and not otherwise.

Hearing the evidence, Flood concluded that the crew had got to the alcohol and gone bananas, apparently forgetting, as everyone else knew, that drinking meths is likely to finish you off. Anyway, he was adamant that the raving boozed-up crew had slaughtered the captain, his family and the ship's officers in a drunken craze. They had then sliced the bows to fake a collision and fled in the lifeboat.

However, analysis of the stains found on the sword and elsewhere showed that they were not blood, possibly much to the disappointment of Mr Flood.

But what had caused the cuts to *Mary Celeste*'s side?

Captain David Williams, a white-bearded sea captain with more than fifty years' ocean-going experience, has come up with an interesting answer to this puzzle. He reports that underwater earthquakes are common around the Azores and that during the severe vibrations of such a seaquake long splints from the ship's recently reconditioned hull could easily have 'popped' from the edges of a few bow planks along the grain, looking as if they had been cut with an unknown instrument.

But whatever the cause, common sense made it obvious that getting off a seaworthy vessel and into a small boat in the middle of the Atlantic in November was unlikely to be something experienced sailors would do without very good reason.

So the question remained: what exactly had happened on the *Mary Celeste*?

————————

The problem

Why had the experienced captain of the *Mary Celeste* abandoned a nice big seaworthy ship full of provisions, for a small, cold, food-free lifeboat miles from anywhere in such a hurry? Had there been some sort of mutiny? Were the crew in a meths-crazed frenzy? Did the ship appear to be sinking? Had it been shaken by a seaquake so terrifying that the crew had fled? Or had something else happened?

Solution on page 200.

THE STORY OF BIG BEN

The mystery

'Big Ben' is the nickname for the so-called 'Great Bell' of the clock at the top of the tower at the Palace of Westminster. Nobody knows where it came from, but it is used by everybody to mean the clock face and the tower itself too.

The clock face and the tower were designed by the architect Augustus Pugin in 1852, but were not finished until 1858, several years after he went bonkers and died. The tower is 315 feet high and has 334 limestone stairs up to the top. Big Ben is owned by the British taxpayer, so any UK citizen who wants to can arrange to be shown round – so long as he or she can make it up those stairs. There is no lift.

The man who designed the workings of the clock was George Biddell Airy, the Astronomer Royal, whose specifications included the following: 'The first stroke of the hour bell should register the time, correct to within one second per day …'

The clock's movement is famously reliable, keeping excellent time by the simple arrangement of a few weights, including an old English penny, that sit on top of the pendulum, which is enclosed in a windproof box. Adding or removing the penny alters the position of the pendulum's centre of mass by a tiny fraction. This changes its effective length and alters the rate at which it swings, and the speed of the hands, by 0.4 seconds per day. With the hour hand measuring nine feet and the minute hand running to fourteen feet, it's a tiny effect, but there are several weights.

Clockmaker John Tricki, who looked after Big Ben on the eve of the Millennium in 1999, said that it takes about half an hour to wind the clock, with a little break to watch the quarter chime. On Millennium Eve, Big Ben was, he said, really spot on. 'The clock went "boing" right on the millisecond of midnight. It was smashing – we were right up the top of the tower with a bottle of champagne and some sandwiches when all the fireworks went off.'

The Great Bell itself, which does the bongs, weighs about as much as a couple of elephants.

Big Ben is part of British life, even for those who live nowhere near it. Its chimes can be heard live, striking the hour before news bulletins on BBC Radio 4, and transmitted around the globe by the BBC World Service. The sound comes via a microphone permanently installed in the tower. The practice of 'live bongs' – if you'll pardon the expression – began in 1923, and, despite some suggestions that a recording would be simpler, the bongs are still transmitted in real time, in good old BBC style.

The problem

How many hands does the clock on the tower of Big Ben have?

Solution on page 202.

THE EUSTON ROAD POISONINGS

The mystery

The Euston Road was opened in 1756 as London's first bypass, running through the capital's outlying fields into the north of the city. But, as London's centre expanded, the Euston Road was absorbed, and it now forms the northern boundary of the city centre, with Regent's Park immediately to its north and University College Hospital just to its south.

In 1954 one of the businesses on Euston Road was a whole-sale chemist's. Among its employees was a 27-year-old typist who had been with the firm since leaving school at 13. She was a pleasant, unambitious woman, who worked in the main office along with twenty or so other people. They were under the direction of a manager who sat in the same room. He was a married 44-year-old veteran of the Royal Army Service corps who had served in Singapore.

On the evening of Monday 26 May the young typist was admitted, seriously ill, to St James's Hospital, Balham, in south London, showing the classic symptoms of severe caustic poisoning. She had eaten normally that day except for a piece of chocolate-covered coconut ice which her office manager, a long-time close friend and confidant, had generously shared around to various people, at about 2.30.

A few minutes after the sweets had been eaten, another of the typists, a 19-year-old former Margate beauty queen, had begun to have stomach pains and feel sick. Before long she was vomiting, and was taken to the first-aid room by the 27-year-old, who was, herself, now very unwell.

The younger woman was given some bicarbonate of soda but complained that this made her feel worse. She had developed a severe burning sensation in her mouth and throat, she could not swallow, and her mouth was blistering so badly that she found it hard to speak.

The older typist was also in trouble. She had severe abdominal pains and had begun vomiting. She too was developing a burning sensation like the younger woman.

The office manager, who had been complaining of a head-ache, now collapsed at his desk. He was not responding, and, like the typists, his cheeks and lips had begun to blister, and his face was becoming discoloured in patches.

An ambulance was called to take the workers to the nearby University College Hospital but the older of the two women decided to go home, so a taxi was ordered. By the time she arrived, at around 6 p.m., she was very pale, and retching uncontrollably. She had to be carried up two flights of stairs where she began vomiting blood.

Her doctor arrived at about 7.30 and was startled by her condition. Finally, now very sick indeed, she agreed to go to hospital, and it was at 9.30, seven hours after first becoming ill, that she was admitted to St James's in a state of collapse, with a rapid pulse, severe pallor and low blood pressure.

This condition, known as 'circulatory shock', or just 'shock', is a life-threatening medical emergency not to be confused with the 'shock' people talk about when they've been surprised by a loud explosion or learnt that they are adopted.

A few miles away, in University College Hospital, the younger typist was in an equally serious condition. Her tongue and mouth were so swollen that doctors were unable to wash out her stomach. Both women were given morphine.

It was by now clear that they had swallowed some severely corrosive poison that was eating away everything from their mouths down to their stomachs.

Mercifully, the office manager had rallied, and was the only one of the victims capable of speaking. Despite his condition, the police, who had been called because of the unexplained nature of the incident, decided to interview him.

He was distressed but suggested that the coconut ice must be to blame. It was certainly suggestive that three of the people who had eaten it had become ill shortly afterwards, although others were showing no signs of poisoning.

The manager was able to describe the sweet shop in Hampstead Road where he had bought the coconut ice. The police visited the shop and confiscated the remaining stock. They also had the paper bag it had come in, along with some uneaten cubes, and had brushed flakes of it from the desks of those who had eaten it. Forensic examination of the uneaten pieces revealed nothing unusual, however.

At University College Hospital there was confusion about what it was that had poisoned these three unhappy people. Acute corrosive poisoning is very uncommon, partly because the immediate burning sensation on contact with the mouth prevents people from swallowing the destructive substance. Such chemicals are, anyway, tightly controlled. Furthermore, the symptoms of corrosive poisoning are immediately apparent, and are not delayed for many minutes, as they had been in this case. Yet here were three victims all succumbing to corrosive poisoning in a wholesale chemist's, where the dangers of such chemicals ought to have been well known.

Thankfully, the office manager, who had been in hospital for three days, had been more fortunate than the women, and his symptoms were improving. Others who had eaten some of the suspicious coconut ice were also feeling all right, and were counting their lucky stars.

The whole sad affair seemed inexplicable. Who would want to poison these two pleasant young ladies and their good friend the office manager? Perhaps it was not deliberate poisoning. Maybe one of the company's chemicals had somehow contaminated the coconut ice. Under analysis, dust from the office manager's desk showed crystals of a poisonous chemical called cantharidin, and in his drawer the police found a pair of scissors with a smear of coconut ice on the blade.

A pharmacist employed by the firm told the police that they did indeed keep a bottle of the deadly chemical in a glass cupboard in his own office. He said that a small amount seemed to have gone missing and that a person – whom he identified – had come in on the day or the poisoning to ask if he could have some to kill some rabbits. This person had later been seen alone in the pharmacist's room.

The problem

Who had poisoned the three victims at the Euston Road wholesale chemists? Was this a case of murder? Or, if it was an accident, what on earth had happened?

Solution on page 202.

KENTUCKY BLUES

The mystery

In 1960 Madison Cawein III, a young haematologist at the University of Kentucky's Lexington medical clinic, began to hear incredible stories about something funny going on in a remote part of the state.

A woman had come in for a blood test and she was blue from head to toe. When it was pointed out to her that her face and fingernails were 'almost indigo' she blithely announced that she was one of the 'Blue Combses' of Ball Creek.

It turned out that Kentucky's Troublesome Creek and Ball Creek had for a long time been home to many people with blue skin. Madison Cawein made it his mission to track down these people and identify, if he could, what was making them this strange colour.

Then one day, two blue people, Patrick and Rachel Ritchie, arrived at Cawein's clinic. After the formalities, the haemotologist delicately asked them whether they had any other blue relations – possibly the oddest question any doctor has ever put to a patient.

Cawein was told that the Blue People of Kentucky belonged to just a few local families, notably the Fugates, and that for

200 years members of the Blue Fugates had lived in the same remote area of the state, in a settlement so isolated that it lacked even roads.

Apart from their blue colouring, the health of the Blue People was otherwise robust, many of them living into great old age. Cawein suspected that they had a condition known as methaemoglobinemia, caused by raised levels of methaemoglobin, a blue form of haemoglobin, which accounts for the blue tinge of the veins on the back of a pink person's hand.

Methaemoglobinemia is the result of an inherited recessive gene – one that is present in the body but not visible. To display the symptoms a person must inherit a methaemoglobinemia gene from both Mum and Dad. Somebody with just one gene would not display the symptoms, but *could* pass on the gene to his or her own children.

The haemotologist tested the Ritchies for haemoglobin abnormalities, but drew a blank. Then a new report by E.M.

Scott came to his notice. It suggested that the red blood cells of people with methaemoglobinemia were lacking the protective enzyme diaphorase, which in healthy people turns blue methaemoglobin into red haemoglobin.

He tested Zach Fugate, the 76-year-old head of the family, and his blue Aunt Bessie, and found that their blood did indeed lack diaphorase. The Blue People of Kentucky had accumulated so much of the blue molecule that it had overwhelmed their haemoglobin.

The doctor initiated a surprising treatment. He injected them with 100 milligrams of methylene blue, a very blue liquid normally used to treat malaria. Within minutes the blue faded from the Ritchies' skin and for the first time in their lives they were a normal colour, like everybody else around them. Because the effect would be temporary, the doctor prescribed them methylene blue pills to take every day for the rest of their lives. But he warned them to watch out for a weird side effect: their urine would turn blue.

The Blue People of Kentucky went away happy, with the bonus that they now had the ability to perform the most astonishing party trick anyone has ever seen.

———————————

The problem

The cause of the proliferation of blue skin in the people of this very remote part of Kentucky was avoidable. It was connected with their isolation and the way in which they therefore went about their daily lives. It would not have occurred had they lived in a more populated area, and was the result of what you might call a 'lifestyle' factor, though one pressed upon them by their circumstances.

Why were there so many blue people in this remote corner of the state? Exactly what was it about the way the Blue

People lived that turned, and kept, generations of them this unusual colour?

Solution on page 204.

UNCLE BOB'S MAGIC PIPE

The mystery

An old policeman once told me he had never arrested a pipe smoker, and that makes sense, because pipe smokers are peaceable people. As the Algonquin spirit the Great Manitou wisely announced, 'If discord has broken out between two beings, let them smoke together. United by this bond, they will live in peace and friendship thereafter.'

Back in the seventies my uncle Bob used to smoke a pipe wherever he went. He favoured a tobacco called Ogden's Walnut Plug, which came in a juicy black lump that he cut with a penknife before rubbing. It always left a liquorice stain on his thumbs and was, he told me, 90 per cent nicotine.

Another blend Uncle Bob enjoyed was Balkan Sobranie Original Smoking Mixture, which came in a beautiful black and white tin and incorporated Macedonian Yenidje leaves.

Anyway, you always knew when Uncle Bob was in the house even if you couldn't see him. When he was out, striding through Bloomsbury in a stiff rain, hat on and pipe in, he always had a tin of Dunhill's Early Morning Pipe safely aboard. This is a sweet Oriental mixture, pressed into a sky-blue tin decorated with a golden sunburst and crowing cockerel.

Even without a hat, Uncle Bob always smoked in the rain, including in downpours that would have put out a large bonfire.

The problem

My Uncle Bob's pipe had no lid and was in every way an ordinary pipe. He could cross an open field in the pouring rain with it gripped between his teeth, without it going out. He didn't cover it with anything, including a lid, an umbrella, his hat, a roof or his hand. How did he manage this?

Solution on page 205.

THE INCREDIBLE STORY
OF KASPAR HAUSER

The mystery

On 26 May 1828, people going about their business in Nuremberg, Bavaria, noticed a disoriented and anxious teenage boy wandering the streets. He could barely walk and kept repeating that he wanted to be a cavalryman, but was otherwise not much help to mystified onlookers.

The boy had with him an anonymous letter addressed to a Captain von Wessenig, explaining that the author had taken the boy in as a foundling sixteen years previously and had brought him up, teaching him to read and write but never letting him out of his house. The letter went on to say that the boy wished to become a cavalryman, 'as his father was'.

Along with the first letter was another, supposedly written by the boy's mother, years before, when he was an infant. It was addressed to the writer of the first and explained that the baby was named Kaspar, that his date of birth was 30 April 1812, and that his father was dead. The trouble was that, as anyone could see, the two letters were written in the same handwriting.

Young Kaspar was taken to Captain von Wessenig's house. The captain was asked either to take the boy under his wing, or have him hanged – the 1828 equivalent, presumably, of an ASBO.

When Kaspar was asked what on earth was going on he would only say that he didn't know, or burst into tears. He kept repeating, 'I want to be a cavalryman, as my father was,' or 'Horse. Horse.' There was an equine theme going on.

Kaspar was in good physical shape and otherwise normal, but he would eat nothing but bread and water. It was suggested that he had been raised as a wolf-child in the forest.

His own account of his history went this way. For as long as he could recall, he said, he had been kept alone in a dark cell containing only a straw bed and a wooden horse. He woke each day to find bread and water beside him, which sometimes tasted bitter. After drinking the bitter water, he would fall into a deep sleep and he would awake with his hair and finger-nails cut.

He never saw or heard another human being until, one day, a mysterious man who concealed his face taught him how to walk, and how to write his name. The stranger instructed him to repeat the sentence, 'I want to be a cavalryman, as my father was,' before releasing him onto the streets of Nuremberg.

This story sounded crazy, with a capital K, but it caused an international sensation.

Kaspar Hauser was put into the care of a teacher, Friedrich Daumer, who looked after him at his house, where he made huge strides in all subjects. But on 17 October 1829 he failed to come to lunch and was discovered in the cellar, bleeding from a cut to his forehead.

He said he had been attacked by a hooded man while on the toilet, and recognised the man's voice as that of the stranger who had kept him in the darkened cell.

He was transferred into the care of Johann Biberbach and his wife.

On 3 April 1830 a pistol shot was heard from Hauser's room and he was found bleeding from a minor wound to the right side of his head. He explained that he had got onto a chair to reach some books but had accidentally taken hold of a pistol that was hanging on the wall, causing it to go off.

Johann Meyer of Ansbach then took over his care, but this relationship was not a good one (nobody managed to spend much time in Hauser's company). On 9 December 1833 the two had a row after Meyer objected to him telling lies. Five days later Kaspar Hauser came home with a deep wound to the left side of his chest. He said that a stranger had lured him into the Ansbach Court Garden and shown him a mysterious bag, before suddenly stabbing him.

The police searched the garden and found a purse containing a note written in mirror writing sprinkled with dashes. In translation it reads:

Hauser can tell you exactly what I look like and where I
am from. To save Hauser the trouble, I want to tell you
myself where I am from - - -. I come from - - - the
Bavarian - - On the river - - - - - I even want to tell you
the name: M. L. Ö.

What the point of this note was supposed to be was anyone's
guess, but it was academic. Kaspar Hauser died of his wound on
17 December 1833. His headstone was inscribed, in Latin, 'Here
lies Kaspar Hauser, riddle of his time. His birth and death
unknown secrets.'

_____

The problem

Who was Kaspar Hauser? Who was the mysterious masked
man who brought him up in a darkened cell? Who was the
murderous man in the Ansbach Court Garden? The answers to
these questions require lateral thinking as well as a good
dollop of common sense.

Solution on page 205.

THE GREAT EPPING
JAUNDICE MYSTERY

The mystery

On Tuesday 9 February 1965, at St Margaret's Hospital, Epping,
in Essex, consultant physician Dr Harry Kopelman was asked
for advice by a 23-year-old medical student. The young man said
he was suffering from something strange that he didn't recognise from his studies.

It had all begun on the Saturday before, at home in Harrow where he lived with his wife. He had started feeling ill, developing pains across the top of his abdomen, which became so severe that he was taken by ambulance to a local casualty department. After examination he was sent home with a vague diagnosis of acute gastritis – inflammation of the stomach – a common symptom, with a range of causes. Oddly, the man's wife was reporting similar, though milder, symptoms, but he was ill enough to have missed work on Monday.

By the time of his consultation with Dr Kopelman the young doctor was over the worst but was still quite unwell, with a sore abdomen, just below the ribs, and a raised temperature. Most peculiarly, he had developed jaundice and was starting to turn an interesting shade of yellow.

Jaundice is a symptom of several disorders, and is caused by a build-up in the blood and body tissues of a liver product called bilirubin. Its yellowing effects are noticeable in the colour of bruises and also of urine. Jaundice itself is associated with ailments including hepatitis, chronic heavy drinking and gallstones. But Dr Kopelman was puzzled by the uncommon pattern of symptoms being presented in this young student doctor, so he had him admitted to the hospital and sent off blood samples for analysis.

In the meantime he went off to his regular outpatient clinic at the Princess Alexandra Hospital in nearby Harlow. No sooner had he unpacked his stethoscope than his assistant reported that his young wife, also a doctor, was feeling very unwell – she had just gone down with jaundice.

Was this a coincidence or the next case of some new and unusual 'doctors' jaundice'? To be on the safe side, Dr Kopelman contacted a local GP to see whether he had noticed any cases of jaundice in his patients. The doctor said it was odd he should ask, because he had recorded six new cases of 'a funny sort of jaundice'.

Kopelman quickly arranged to visit all these patients, each of whom was, curiously, one half of a yellowing married couple. They were all well-to-do professional men and women: doctors, teachers, solicitors. Of the first sixty cases none was a young child, and just six were in their teens.

Harry Kopelman alerted the Medical Officer of Health for the area, Dr Isidore Ash. But Dr Ash was already aware that something peculiar was going on, with several cases of 'Epping Jaundice' having sprung up in Harlow, and a hotspot in the village of Chipping Ongar, not far away.

At St Margaret's Hospital, the wife of the medical student had herself now gone yellow. After five days since her initial discomfort, the pain had subsided to be replaced by fever and jaundice, just like her husband. This was typical of the pattern. After acute onset of pain, which would last for two or three days, there would be a pause of a few days, during which the patient would feel generally unwell, before the jaundice worsened, bringing with it an intolerable itching of the skin.

Some possibilities were already ruled out. No patient had signs of gall-bladder problems, and none of the victims had liver fluke. In a cold February an insect-borne disease seemed highly unlikely. None of the blood samples revealed a case of 'rat-catchers' yellows', a rare jaundice resulting from Weil's disease, spread by rodents. Indeed, all the patients, so far, lived in the pleasant low-rat-index towns and villages around Epping. Infection of any kind seemed out of the question – no known infection or poison produced this singular pattern of effects.

A new virus seemed unlikely because none of the affected couples knew any of the others; and none of them had shared a meal outside their home or been to any social occasion with any of them, where they could have passed it on.

Nonetheless, Dr Kopelman wondered whether the cause of the Epping Jaundice could be something the patients had all eaten. There was nothing out of the ordinary. Their diet was what you would expect in 1965 in this prosperous, educated slice of society. They were eating a wide range of healthy foods, including wholemeal bread.

The Epping Jaundice was unique in its presentation, and in its appearance under the microscope, for every victim showed inflammation of the tiny bile ducts of the liver, in a pattern never before seen.

It was beginning to look as if the damage to the liver suffered by victims of the Epping Jaundice could only be the result of injury from some chemical or drug. Was there some new product that these well-off patients had all started using? Maybe it could be alcohol, or tobacco, or the still novel contraceptive pill?

But it seemed not – half the patients were men, and smokers and drinkers suffered no more than their abstinent fellow victims.

Dr Kopelman knew that whatever was causing the new jaundice was limited to the area around Epping. There were no reports of the disease from elsewhere in the country. But the Epping Jaundice was affecting only certain people in this area. They tended to be adults, they tended to be couples, and they tended to be professional.

Then Kopelman's mind wandered back to the young student doctor and his wife. Unlike the other patients, they lived in Harrow, some 30 miles away, and only *he* regularly came into Epping. Harrow itself seemed to be unaffected, yet the young doctor's wife had developed the characteristic symptoms of the Epping Jaundice without ever leaving her home town. Had her husband somehow carried the virus, bacterium, drug, chemical or poison all the way from Epping, and brought it into their home?

Harry Kopelman questioned the patient closely but she could think of nothing. The only thing her husband had brought home from Epping the day of her illness was a loaf of wholemeal bread, a loaf they had eaten before without incident.

Then there was a development: another medical professional was brought into the hospital showing the distinctive symptoms of Epping Jaundice. Perhaps this was indeed a 'white coat' disease, favouring doctors and nurses.

The new patient was a nursing sister, and Dr Kopelman spoke to her closely, taking a detailed history. Who had she met? What had she done? Who had she nursed? Where had she been, and when? What had she eaten? What pills had she taken?

It was a long and painstaking conversation but, while going through her list of groceries, the patient mentioned in passing that she had bought some wholemeal bread a day or two before starting to feel unwell. Harry Kopelman pricked up his ears and, excusing himself, excitedly shot along to the bedside of another Epping Jaundice patient. He had an important question for her. Before becoming ill had she eaten any wholemeal bread? The answer was revealing – no, she had only eaten sliced white bread. Was she sure she hadn't bought or eaten any brown bread? She was certain. White sliced bread only.

The problem

What was causing the Epping Jaundice? Was it some new disease that professional people, especially doctors and nurses, particularly came into contact with? Why did it seem to be singling out couples? Why were some people getting it and not others? Why was it confined to the areas around Epping, and why was there one solitary case in Harrow, 30 miles away? Was it the wholemeal bread that was somehow responsible?

Solution on page 206.

THE FASTEST SUBMARINE IN THE WORLD

The mystery

Ever since Leonardo da Vinci sketched out an experimental design for a submarine, the possibility of a real underwater boat has been the dream of men in sheds at the bottom of their gardens.

A proposal for the first true underwater craft was written in 1578 by William Bourne, a British naval nut who suggested a completely enclosed vessel, looking rather like two rowing boats glued together, which could be rowed underwater.

Even by the time of the First World War, submarines were still not all that brilliant. They had no periscope and had to keep coming up to the top to see where they were. In 1921 an American sub ran out of fuel, and the crew had to put up sails made out of sailors' blankets and curtain rods, before sailing 100 miles to port.

But modern submarines are much more sophisticated vessels, as quiet as the ocean itself, even though they are so huge. They can submerge in less than a minute and stay down for six months. The nuclear-powered ones (that's most of them) can go 60,000 miles on just one lump of uranium the size of a walnut, and dive to a depth of more than 800 feet. This is equivalent to floating in the air at two and a half times the height of Big Ben. Even so, they still use a large pipe to suck clean air from the surface, rather like a snorkelling holidaymaker.

Although the submarines of today can go very fast, the speed performance of the USS *Skate* is astonishing. On 17 August 1958 this submarine really showed what she was made of when she did a circumnavigation of the globe in just fifty minutes.

The problem

How on earth did the USS *Skate*, one of the earliest nuclear-powered submarines, go around the world in less than an hour?

Solution on page 208.

LATERAL THINKING
BETCHAS AND GOTCHAS

'Sometimes the situation is only a problem
because it is looked at in a certain way.'
Edward de Bono

THE COCKTAIL GLASS

The bet

This beautiful little demonstration is one of the finest and most
brain-curdling lateral thinking problems I know.

What you do is arrange four matches in the shape of a cock-
tail glass, as illustrated in the picture below.

Next, break off the end of a match and drop it into the position shown, to represent an olive.

Bet your audience that they can't move just two matches such
that the olive ends up outside the glass. They are not allowed to
touch the olive or end up with a damaged-looking glass.

If you are doing this for men you can tell them that the object is a spade with the broken piece of match representing a stone.

You can set up the betcha with this amusing story about a builder.

An Irishman goes for a job on a building site in London. The foreman says, 'This is a high-class construction site. We don't just accept anyone here; you'll have to answer some hard questions before we can accept you.'

'OK,' says the Irishman.

'Right,' says the foreman. 'What's the difference between a joist and a girder?'

The Irishman sucks his teeth for a second.

'Simple!' he says. 'Joyce wrote *Ulysses* and Goethe wrote *Faust*.'

This is a beautiful lateral thinking joke, because people are expecting an anti-Irish joke and they get an intellectual pro-Irish joke instead.

Anyway, you then bet them that they can't move just two matches to leave the stone beside the spade. They mustn't touch the stone, and the spade must be exactly the same shape when they've finished.

———————————

The chicanery

The solution is illustrated below. First you slide the horizontal match halfway, so its end meets the tip of the central match. Next you move the original left-hand match down to the bottom right-hand position indicated in the illustration.

Working this out takes quite a bit of thinking. It's a lovely little puzzle.

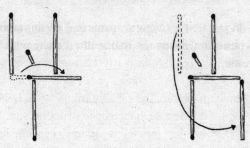

NAILED IT!

The bet

A fellow I know, who is a magician, was one day working at home with a mechanical saw, making a piece of magical appa-ratus. He was cutting away merrily when he absent-mindedly amputated one of his index fingers. They fixed him up at the hospital but they couldn't reattach the finger.

Not only has the absence of this finger since impeded his nose-picking capacities, it has affected his ability to shuffle cards and produce rabbits from top hats, as you might imagine. You'd never normally know he was missing a finger, though, because they gave him a prosthetic one. The join is hidden by a ring, and it can be disconcerting to see him suddenly pull the thing off to show it to someone, or wiggle it vigorously in a very unnatural-looking way.

He could say something like, 'I bet you ten quid I can scratch my left elbow with my left index finger.' People would sneer and pour opprobrious scoffs upon him. Then he would simply pop the thing off with his right hand and scratch his elbow.

While I was thinking about this it occurred to me how similar the effect would be to an old fraud described by the puzzle-loving mathematician Martin Gardner in one of his many superb books.

What happens is that you bet your audience that you can remove your own thumbnail. Then, taking out your pocket-knife you do just that, causing screams and groans among your most nervous admirers as the nail is lifted away with horrible verisimilitude.

———————

The chicanery

This gruesome trick needs a bit of preparation. The beauty of it, though, is that you can prepare long in advance of your demonstration.

What you do is apply a coating of melted candle wax to your thumbnail, using a small brush. It dries quickly and sticks fast, looking just like an actual nail.

When the time comes for your betcha, make the bet, then remove the pocket-knife and slide it slowly under the wax, lifting it away in a revoltingly realistic manner. If you are a gifted actor, you will be able to make pained grimaces like Laurence Olivier while you do this, which will add to the theatrical charm of the performance.

I've added to the realism of this when doing it myself by first surreptitiously jabbing a sharp needle into the skin close to the nail. This part of the thumb is poorly supplied with nerve endings, so it doesn't hurt much. The wound should not produce blood until the finger is squeezed, so if you time it right you can squeeze gently at the appropriate moment and it will ooze quite an impressive amount of blood just as the fake nail is coming away, and will run around the cuticle and under the wax in a delightfully disgusting manner.

Paraffin wax is edible, so if you wish to add a touch of the truly macabre to the already grisly effect, you can drop the fake nail into your mouth, blood and all, and swallow it, though this is not recommended on a first date.

If you're betting for money, or a drink or something, insist on receiving your payment before you start, because once you've done the trick and got the screams, some bright spark will spot that you still have a nail on the end of your thumb.

FIVE INTO FOUR *WILL* GO

The bet

Did you hear about the man in the hot air balloon? He was floating over the countryside when he realised he was completely lost, so he dropped down a bit and shouted to a fellow he could see walking along a lane.

'You, there,' he called. 'Can you tell me where I am?'

The man shouted back up, 'You are in a hot air balloon, sir, 40 feet above the ground, 53 degrees 24 minutes north and 2 degrees 58 minutes west.'

'My God, that's accurate,' said the balloonist. 'Are you an engineer?'

'That's right,' said the man. 'How did you know?'

'Well,' he said, 'everything you just told me may be technically accurate but I still have absolutely no idea where the bloody hell I am. To be honest, you're about as much use as a one-legged man at an arse-kicking party.'

'There's no need to be rude,' replied the engineer. 'By the way, are you by any chance a manager?'

'How did you know that?' shouted the balloonist, fiddling with the burner.

'Easy,' said the man. 'You haven't got a clue where you are, or what you're doing, you've risen to your position by nothing more than hot air, and now that you're in a muddle you're expecting someone below you to solve your stupid problem for you. In fact, you're in exactly the same position you were before we had this delightful chat, but now somehow it's *my* fault.'

This joke reminded me of that unlikely lateral thinking scenario often presented to staff on team-building awaydays. Five famous people are floating in a hot air balloon above the sea. They are Diego Maradona, Joanna Lumley, Albert Einstein, Hillary Clinton and David Beckham. They are losing altitude and unless one person is sacrificed they will all crash into the water and drown. It's the job of members of the team to work out who exactly should be thrown over the edge.

Of course, there's only one sensible answer, which is Albert Einstein. All the others are still alive and he's already dead.

The problem is called 'Five into four won't go', but in this fiendish little match betcha you can show that five into four *will* go.

What you do is set up sixteen matches in the pattern of five squares shown below.

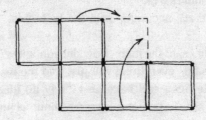

Now tell your helper or helpers that they must move two matches to leave four squares, the same size as you started with. They may not take any matches away. All sixteen must form part of the final pattern.

The chicanery

No chicanery, exactly. The mystery as presented is completely straight and honest. It may not be a trick question, but neither is it one that is going to be solvable by logical thinking – you have to come at it sideways. The arrows in the diagram reveal the solution.

This is a terrific match problem, and one of the best. In fact, you can even demonstrate the solution and then set the puzzle up again but *upside down*. Then watch as your spectator tries to solve the thing until his brain falls out through his ear.

THE KISS

The bet

What you do is take two matches from a box and push one upright, into the top of the box towards one end on an imaginary centre line, in the position shown below.

Borrow a thin ring and place it on top of the box, as drawn.

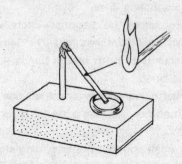

Now begin your tale.

'These canoodling couples should be more careful in busy places like this,' you say. 'A girl had her handbag nicked in here the other day by a fellow standing right behind her, even though she'd put her leg through the strap, like this.' Position the second match with its 'foot' inside the ring, as shown, and its head resting on top of the head of the upright match. It's slightly fiddly but not too difficult.

'Now,' you continue, 'you'd think that it would be impossible to steal the handbag without cutting the handle, but our thief was a superb tactician who had done this before.

'I bet you I can take this ring without touching these matches, or moving them from their present position – just like the thief who managed to steal the bag without the lady noticing. Who's willing to bet me that I can't do it?'

Everyone will be agog now, so take your time.

The chicanery

Continue your little story like this: 'Our lady was leaning against "Lover Boy", all gooey, and he gave her a really *hot* kiss, like this.' Take a second box of matches from your pocket and strike a match. You must use a second matchbox for this bit or you will knock your 'lady' over.

Hold the flame under the diagonal match, about a quarter of the way down, until it catches light. The flame will creep up the slanted match until both match heads suddenly ignite, causing them to bond.

Shortly thereafter the female match will bend in the centre, dramatically lifting her 'leg' like a starlet being kissed something fierce.

Say, 'That's when she lost her bag,' and slip the ring out, returning it to its owner. Blow out the matches artistically and claim your winnings.

TWELVE MINUS TWO EQUALS TWO

The bet

Mathematicians have their own language, and their own in-jokes, like the one about the plant on the maths teacher's desk that grew square roots. I also like this one – Question: How do you make seven an even number? Answer: Take the S out – which is a lateral thinking joke as much as it is a number joke.

Mathematicians love squares. The square is a fascinating shape, and its perpendicularity has led to its being used to represent honesty and straightness since the 1500s. It was only in the 1940s that it began to be used to refer to conventionality, but by the sixties young long-haired people were 'with it' and 'groovy', while bald cardigan-wearing pipe-smokers were 'without it', or, curse of curses, 'square'.

The square crops up in many match puzzles, and this one is one of the simplest to understand but hardest to work out.

What you do first is make the shape below. It looks like the end of a Battenburg cake, or somebody's window. You then bet that your assistant/s cannot remove two matches from the arrangement and leave just two squares. Cor, it isn't half difficult.

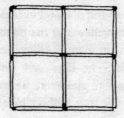

The chicanery

The answer to the puzzle looks ridiculously simple when you see it (illustrated below), but it is hard for your victims to work out for themselves because the mind has a tendency to group similar things together. So, when you say to them 'two squares', they subconsciously think, 'two squares of the same size'.

The more abstract thinkers will see the answer quickly, but there again they will have clothes that don't fit, wonky hair and no sense of humour. They may even be square. It's swings and roundabouts when it comes to personality, in this life.

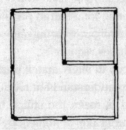

NINE PLUS NOTHING MAKES TEN

The bet

Show your victim a handful of matches. Ask him to hold out his hand and pour the matches into his palm. Say, 'Count these matches slowly into my hand.' Allow him to do this. 'How many?' you ask. 'Nine,' he says. Ask him how many more matches he would need to make ten. He will say that he needs one more match. Bet him that, without breaking any matches or adding any more, you can count them onto the table and show him you actually have ten.

The chicanery

This is lateral thinking at its purest. What you have said so far is absolutely true, although in writing it is not quite true. This is because I should have put inverted commas around 'ten' because what you do is count down the matches one at a time onto the table to form the pattern illustrated:

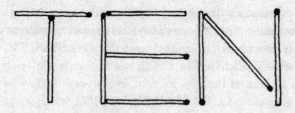

You do this by laying down the vertical matches first, counting slowly, 'One, two, three, four ...' Then quickly put down the horizontals, 'five-six-seven-eight ...', then the diagonal, 'nine', and finish with a resounding 'Ten!' as you point to the word. This showy presentation adds a bit of suspense to a delightful bald-faced cheat, building the drama and preventing your victim from guessing too soon what it is you are up to. As in many lateral thinking puzzles of this sort, you must choose your words carefully. Don't say, 'I can count these onto the table and have ten matches.' That would be untrue and unfair.

Don't forget to smile as you take the money.

BETTING EDGE

The bet

The £2 coin is the only British coin made in two pieces, from two metals of different colours. The outer yellowish ring is made mainly of copper with a bit of nickel and zinc; the silver-coloured inner disc is made mainly of copper with a bit of nickel but no zinc. This is the first British coin to be made of two distinct bits since the 1692 tin farthing with a copper plug.

Around the outside edge of the £2 coin is an inscription that nobody ever reads. In pre-2015 coins this says, STANDING ON THE SHOULDERS OF GIANTS, from a famous remark by Isaac Newton. Around the new £2 coin, introduced in 2015, is the Latin inscription QUATUOR MARIA VINDICO, which translates as, 'I will claim the four seas,' a more pompous, less modest and rather expansionist-sounding legend.

The coin is pleasantly weighty and is nice to handle. It is easy enough to balance on edge on a flat surface if you hold it between your thumb and fingers. But if you try to do this, holding the coin by its outer edge with the tips of your two index fingers, it is remarkably difficult. Try it, and you'll see. However, once you know the secret it can be done.

Trying to put the coin down without your fists on the table causes an invisible but significant wobble, which is magnified by the fingers, so here's how you should do it. First, you must plant your curled fists together, thumbs-up on the table with the index fingers extended, holding the coin.

Next, touch the coin to the table and, looking directly from above it, get it absolutely upright. It's tricky but practice helps. Once it appears steady, press it slightly from opposite sides.

Now carefully release the finger of your dominant hand, leaving the coin touching the other index finger. It will be held slightly by the finger's natural moistness.

Finally, carefully pull the supporting finger away from the coin. Sometimes it will topple over but usually it will stay upright.

OK, this is all very well, but what is the bet?

The bet is that you will give your victim £1 for every coin he can balance in this way. If he can't he pays you nothing.

The Chicanery

First you must borrow a £2 coin from the spectator to show what you mean. But when you demonstrate, don't rest your hands on the table and don't release the coin. Just say, 'Hold the coin like this with your outstretched fingers, put it down on the table and leave it balanced on edge, and I'll give you £1 for every coin you can balance. If you fail you don't have to give me anything.'

It sounds like a terrific bet and your victim will have a couple of goes, probably failing. So do it yourself, this time anchoring your fists on the table as described earlier. Make it clear, without saying, just how you are steadying the coin. If your sucker is not watching closely enough, make it very obvious. Volunteers soon spot what you're up to and try to copy your technique.

After a couple of goes they will do it and will be punching the air in victory. If they want another go, say that they must leave the balanced coin where it is, and use another £2 coin from their purse or pocket.

Three successes is plenty, so once they've succeeded say, 'Well done. I'm going to give you a pound for each coin you balanced, as I said. You've balanced three [let's say] coins, so here's £3.'

As they take your money, reach over and pocket their three £2 coins. When they object, say, 'I said I'd give you £1 for each coin, and I have.'

You've made £3 on the bet. Be ready to run for it.

THE HOUSE MOVE

The bet

There is a wonderful problem with matches that involves the construction of a matchstick house.

You begin by telling your audience a story about an ordinary-looking house that had a roof and four sides, and looked like the representation of the house shown below, which you make using eleven matches.

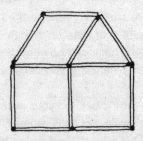

You say that there was a window in each wall of the house and that each window faced south. One day a bear walked past one of the windows. The question is, 'What colour was the bear?'

The answer is a classic of lateral thinking. It is to do with the odd assertion that each window of the house faced south. How could that be? Normally each wall of a square house would face in one of four different directions. They can't all face the same way.

Actually, 'all facing the same way' is not the same thing as, 'all facing south', for at the North Pole every direction is, indeed, south. So, if the house was precisely over the North Pole, the bear passing the window would have to be a polar bear. Therefore the colour of the bear must be white.

While your victims are cursing you for this knotty problem, you pose another puzzler. You tell them that your matchstick house is now a log cabin in Nebraska, and that it faces *west* (marked with a W).

The matchstick man who lives in the house loves the morning sun, which comes up in the east, so he doesn't like his house facing west, as it does. But neither does he have enough money to make any big structural alterations to the residence, so he decides, by moving just one match, to adjust the building so that instead of facing west it faces east, towards the morning sun.

Bet your spectators that they can't move one match to make the house face east instead of west.

———————

The chicanery

There's a kind of beauty to the simplicity and subtlety of the answer to this puzzle. The diagram below shows what you do.

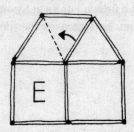

And you didn't have to ring round a lot of builders.

BLIND DATE

The bet

In his autobiography the philosopher Bertrand Russell said, 'I have tried to apprehend the Pythagorean power by which number holds sway above the flux,' which seems like quite a task for a Monday morning.

Numbers are interesting and there is even a theory knocking about that they have a mystical relationship with events. This idea is called numerology, and, along with other pseudo-scientific theories, it has been used by stock market analysts as well as outright charlatans – but I repeat myself. Anyway, the point of all this is that you can use the idea yourself in the following coin betcha.

Give your audience a spiel about numerology and how mysterious and important it is. You can if you like quote the enigmatic numerological links between Presidents Lincoln and Kennedy: Abraham Lincoln was elected to the House of Representatives in 1846, John Fitzgerald Kennedy was elected to the House exactly 100 years later; in 1946; Lincoln was elected President in 1860, Kennedy was elected President in 1960, precisely 100 years later; both presidents fathered four children; both presidents had seven letters in their last name; Lincoln's assassin had fifteen letters in his name, Kennedy's alleged assassin had fifteen letters in his name. It's quite a list.

Here's a little betcha that uses the idea of numerology to confuse people.

The chicanery

Announce that you will leave the room, or turn your back, and that if anybody will place a coin face down on the table and cover it with his or her hand, you will be able to name the date immediately, owing to the numerological propensity of coins. (This doesn't mean a damn thing but sounds marvellous.) It's £1 each to watch the demonstration.

Collect the spectators' fees in your hat (if you wear one), and look away or leave while a coin is placed on the table and hidden under somebody's hand.

When you are told that everything's ready, turn round or come back into the room and make the Rodin's *Thinker* pose, with your knuckles to your brow. After a suitably dramatic pause, say, 'Yes, I'm seeing the date ... Yes ... It's ... It's ...', and then just announce the date on which you are perpetrating this outrage.

MAGNETIC MATCHES

The bet

Tell your spectators about magnetism. Actually, don't do this, because it's a very hard subject to explain, especially if you've had a couple of large ones. Instead just give them a bit of history.

Although people have been aware of magnets and magnetic properties for thousands of years, it was a chap named William Gilbert (1540–1603) who first investigated magnetism in a scientific way. One of his discoveries was that the earth itself is a magnet. He must have had a really huge one himself to find that out.

Tell your assembled admirers that, although it is usually metals containing iron that are magnetic, you have discovered how to magnetise anything, by using the ferric properties of your hair. 'I can even magnetise wooden matches,' you say.

You hand a match to one of your spectators and ask them to rub it through your hair (if you have any). They then do the same with the other match.

When they have done this you touch the head of one match to the head of the other, which you are holding upright, and pause dramatically for a second. Then you let go with the fingers that are holding the top match. Miraculously, the two are now attracted to each other, with the top one seemingly stuck to the bottom one. You explain that this is not balance, if that's what people are thinking, but magnetic attraction. You say you can even turn the two matches upside down without the top match falling off, and you do so.

When the amazed silence becomes too much for everyone to bear, you pull the matches apart with a little magnetic pop.

You now bet your victims that nobody else can do the trick. They may try, but they won't be able to do it, unless they know – or are laterally minded enough to work out – the sneaky secret.

———————

The chicanery

The trick to this lovely little betcha is that match heads become slightly sticky when wet. If you lick the top of one and then press it firmly against another the two will be lightly attached.

The way you make use of this secret is to take your two matches in your left hand (if right-handed) and hand one match to a spectator with your right hand. You need to be seated to do this effectively.

Keep the other match held upright between the fingers of your left hand as you bend forwards to offer the top of your head for them to rub their match through your hair, or on your scalp if you're as bald as my Uncle Bob. Bend far forwards so that your nose is almost touching the table.

When they have finished, sit up and switch matches, taking theirs and giving them yours. Bend forwards again and get them to repeat the business with the second match. There will be a lot of giggling during all this, which you should encourage.

As their attention is focused on what they are doing, briefly insert the end of your match between your lips. Don't leave it in there for ages, as it's not a recommended food. A swift lick should do it. Your helpers will not be able to see this because of your bent head, and because of the attention they are paying to what they are doing. This is what magicians call 'misdirection'.

When your helper has finished, sit up and take back their match. Now push it *hard*, head to head with the match in your hand. The wetness will cause the two to stick together, but this can take a moment or two. To disguise the pressure you may need to exert, conceal the matches from your helpers by pushing them together behind the first two fingers of each hand. Once they are stuck they will stay stuck, and you can release your hold with the top hand.

As you let go, your acting ability takes over. You should appear to be concentrating hard on what you are doing. Pass the magnetised matches between hands a couple of times, before finally popping them apart.

Holding them as a pair, immediately strike them together on the box, saying, 'And look: they still strike.' Doing this gets rid of the slightly sticky evidence.

Now empty out a few more matches onto the table and challenge others to attempt the magnetising business with their hair. Ten minutes of fun can be got out of this bit.

THE GLASS MOUSETRAPS

The bet

The glass mousetraps is an ancient lateral thinking scam that must be one of the most shameless ever. The effect from the victim's point of view is that a simple experiment is explained whereby he must 'catch' three 'mice' with three glasses in just three moves. When he tries to repeat the simple moves he's been shown he is unable to succeed.

Start by arranging three glasses in a row on the bar or table between yourself and your victim: the centre glass mouth-down, the end glasses mouth-up. In front of each glass you place a paper ball, olive, peanut, coin or other suitable object to represent your mice.

When you're set, explain: 'Look, I bet you can't catch these three mice under these three glass mousetraps in just three moves. I'll show you how it's done first, to help you, and then you can have a go. But I move fast, so watch carefully.'

You now lift any two glasses – one in each hand – and turn them both over, putting any mouth-down glass over its mouse and replacing any mouth-up glass in its original position behind its mouse. The glass mousetraps remain associated with their original mice throughout and mustn't hop about. You say: 'One.'

You then turn over two glasses again, placing any mouth-down glass over its mouse, saying: 'Two.'

Finally, for the third time, you turn over two glasses and finish with each mouse under a mouth-down glass. You say: 'Three.' You have captured three mice in three moves.

You can demonstrate the effect two or three times, using different variations to get the result you want. Stay awake, though, because it's possible to get your head in a mess and screw things up.

In fact, the scam can easily be done in just two moves, but by allowing a third move you complicate matters to the point where your spectator's brain starts to turn to custard.

Once you are clear that your victim understands the rules, set up the glasses for him. It is at this point that the monkey business occurs.

———————

The chicanery

What you appear to do when you come to arrange things for your victim to have a go is replace the glass mousetraps behind their mice in the original start position. What you really do is move all the glasses back to their start point but make sure that the middle glass – number two – is *mouth-up* and the outer glasses are *mouth-down*. This is the reverse of the original set-up, where the middle glass was *mouth-down*. No matter how hard your volunteer now tries, he cannot cover the mice without doing something that isn't allowed – even if he goes on all night.

After a couple of drinks his lateral thinking capacities will be dulled and the look on his face will be wonderful to behold as he racks his brains and wonders what's gone wrong.

Take the money and run.

FIRE UNDER WATER

The bet

Make a grand bet with your admiring followers that you can create an underwater fire in a full glass or jug. Announcements like this are of the 'witch-doctor' or 'charismatic-temple-leader' sort. People may bow down, burst into tears, or beg to go to bed with you, which can't be bad. If they don't ask to do any of these you can simply claim money for your entertaining show.

There are two ways of producing this effect, one genuinely flammable, scientific and startling, the other easier but more in the nature of a lateral thinking liberty-taking with meaning. Both are fun in their own way.

The chicanery

The first method for producing this effect is suitable only for sheds or 'patio demonstrations' in fair weather, because it involves the use of a sparkler.

Sparklers contain a number of interesting ingredients to make them work, including various metals and, importantly for this demonstration, so-called 'oxidisers'. Oxidisers increase the rate of burning when the sparkler is lit. Potassium nitrate, barium nitrate and strontium nitrate are all common oxidisers in sparklers. Though these nitrates are not themselves combustible, they enhance the burning of other substances, and this is the key to making your bet work.

If you were to light a sparkler and dip it into a cup or jug of water it would go out. However, because of the oxidisers, the sparkler will continue to burn under water if you wrap a single spiral of Scotch tape around it before lighting it with a match, or, better, another sparkler. It will then burn away fast and furious under water.

What the tape does, in case you are interested, is provide an effective waterproof barrier around the sparkler. The oxidisers are so powerful that this barrier is enough to allow them to burn despite the water. The tape itself will melt from the intense heat as the sparkler does its thing.

The other, easier method can be done impromptu in the house, in a restaurant or down the pub.

At a romantic dinner with a person you have high hopes for, you can say something like, 'You have provocative eyes, like those of an Egyptian princess (prince). This candle brings out their hot, mysterious beauty.'

Cheap flattery of this kind always works a treat. Anyway, you continue, 'Did you know that candles can burn under water?' No matter what the reply, you say, 'Look, I bet you a kiss that I can make this candle burn under water without it going out. Let me show you.'

Once you've got the go-ahead, pick up the candle in your right hand and immediately lift your glass of water in your left. Place the candle under the glass of water. 'There, it worked,' you say.

Another way to do this is to do the lateral thinking bet first and then follow up with the sparkler demonstration – when you are somewhere suitable, obviously. Don't start lighting fireworks in restaurants, it's not the done thing. Also, don't do this if you are not an adult. Obviously! Matches and sparklers must be handled with great care, as Joan of Arc said to the man with the lighted taper.

This double-show is five minutes of entertaining lateral thinking and hooey, plus a couple of free drinks, or whatever you care to bet.

SAUCER SORCERY

The bet

I remember once seeing a beggar in San Francisco who was doing some simple magic tricks for passers-by. He wasn't 100 per cent washed but he was trying his hardest and was evidently earning enough to pay for a few cans of dinner. People are far readier to fork out for a guy like this than they are for some homunculus squatting in a corner, glaring into the pavement. It is a pleasant characteristic of most people that they don't mind reaching into their pocket if they are being entertained at the same time. They feel they are getting something in return for their donation.

Restaurants and cafés are often good places to use this principle, and the following cheeky scam will entertain your friends and win you a brandy or two at the same time.

Many restaurants these days seem to have an unhealthy thirst for novelty, which may be related to their penchant for giving fairly ordinary dishes fancy foreign names. Once upon a time you could identify restaurant food by what it was called: liver and bacon, roast chicken, potatoes, cabbage, haddock, green salad, trifle, spotted dick, Cheddar, Beaujolais, black coffee. But now I don't know what the hell anything is in some places. 'Assiette of piglet' is, I find, common or garden pork served on a plate (novel idea), while 'Petits pois à la française' is apparently just French-style peas. But maybe there's method in this madness. Stanford University's Prof. Dan Jurafsky found that dishes described with longer words cost 11p per letter more.

On the whole, cafés are better than restaurants in this respect: there's not much you can do to gentrify egg, chips and a mug of tea. There used to be a place near me once, called Anu's Café, where Anu, trying to be with-it, removed the pound signs and punctuation marks from his prices. A cup of tea marked on the board at '120' looked like £120 to me. He also tried tarting up his coffee with names like Americana, Crappuccino, Latte and all that nonsense. Someone got her own back, though, by nicking the apostrophe from his neon sign. Thereafter, punters seeing 'Anus Café' flashing on and off at the end of the road did not find their mouths watering.

Another annoying novelty in restaurants is square plates. Whose idea was that? For millennia diners have been happily noshing off round plates – who needs corners? Which reminds me what it is that I'm supposed to be telling you about.

It's this jolly bet you can have with some friends in a café or restaurant. When everyone is relaxed and unbuttoned at the end of the meal, and the coffee is finished, you pick up your cup and saucer and say this: 'I bet you a brandy that I can push this saucer through the handle of this cup.' Nobody will believe you, so you repeat, 'Yes, I can poke this saucer right through this cup handle.' Everybody will now be alert and expectant and someone will offer to buy you a brandy if you succeed.

_____

The chicanery

Pick up the cup by its rim and then pick up the saucer. Line up the saucer with the cup handle as if you were going to push the saucer through the handle like a giant needle and thread. Build the suspense a little and then, as if deciding on a better technique, put the saucer down on the table and quickly push your finger through the cup handle, giving the saucer a good poke. 'There,' you say. 'I pushed the saucer through the cup handle.'

You'll get either a groan or a laugh, depending on whether or not you've got friendly friends.

HOW TO PUT YOUR HEAD WHERE YOUR BOTTOM SHOULD BE

The bet

At the bar, choose someone to help you. Compliment your volunteer on his or her nose. Tell them that their conk is a fine example of a masculine Roman nose, or an intellectually aquiline nose, or a fine prizefighter's hooter. Suit your compliments to your subject. This is called 'salesmanship'.

Tell ladies, as you gently run your finger from their glabella down to their supratip break (I had to look those up), that they have the nose of a princess, or a beautiful model, or the perfect example of the retroussé line, indicating breeding, brains and beauty.

Then say, 'My nose runs in the family. You see, I was born upside down – my nose does the running, and my feet do the smelling.' When the gales of laughter die down (shouldn't take more than half an hour), point at your beer and say, 'This Australian lager [you can use any beer with a head] was also born upside down: its head is where its bottom should be and its bottom is where its head should be, rather like the Prime Minister [or Leader of the Opposition, or someone else you know your victim can't stand].'

Now bet your subject that if he (or she) buys you a glass of beer you will be able to put its frothy head at the bottom. Seems impossible, but it's not.

———————————

The chicanery

The solution to this delightful bet is magnificently simple. You need a completely full glass of beer with a small head on it, but don't bother with one of those real ales that contain just one bubble per pint. The glass must have a circumference no bigger than your palm. The gag works very nicely with a half-pint measure.

Do your spiel and accept the beer. Then simply place your flat hand on top of the drink and lift the glass with your other hand, carefully but swiftly turning it over. The head, somewhat surprisingly, stays where it was in relation to the rest of the beer, and is now at the bottom. By the way, this is one of those things you've got to practise at home first.

Obviously don't try to drink the drink without turning it back up again or your famous nose is going to be full of beer. Though I suppose you could always bet them first that you can put your head up your nose.

BEND ME YOUR EARS

The bet

Did you hear the joke about the glazer who was carrying a sheet of glass over his shoulder? He stumbled and the glass slipped, cutting off his ear. The ear fell into a hole where some builders were putting a piling, so the glazer knelt down and bent into the dark hole to ask the men if they could see it. They had a look around until one chap saw the ear bobbing in a puddle. He picked it up, wiped it on his trousers, and dropped it into his hard hat.

'Is this it?' he asked, waving the hat up at the glazer.

'No,' replied the glazer. 'Mine had a pencil behind it.'

Strictly speaking, this isn't a joke about an ear – much of which is concealed inside the skull – it's a joke about just the fleshy visible *outer* ear, which, as almost nobody knows, is called the 'pinna' or 'auricle'.

Some mammals can adjust the direction of their auricles, and, in those with mobile pinnae (such as the horse), the left and right ones can be moved and directed independently of each other. In most humans, however, the outer ears are impossible to move at all, singly or in pairs, and this is the basis of this charming bet.

What you do is announce that you can wiggle your left ear without wiggling your right. Impossible? Ask people to try it. This will provide five minutes of general hilarity while your chums strain and make faces, while trying without success to

move either or both ears. If you have a phone with a camera –
not everybody does, you young readers – take a few pictures
and post them online for the mere pleasure of laughing at your
friends.

Now, before you actually do the demo, it's time to get a drink
bought by those who wish to see your incredible display of
auricular skill.

———————

The chicanery

Once you've got your drink/s bought for you, repeat the details
of the miraculous feat you are about to perform – you are
going to wiggle your left ear without wiggling your right. Now,
ask for a drum roll and grasp your left ear with your hand and
wiggle it vigorously. Done! This is one of those bets where it's
important to claim your prize *before* you do the demonstration. Otherwise people might feel inclined to break their
contract with you, on the ground that you deliberately misled
them. Either that or you might go home with both your ears
displaying cauliflower tendencies.

THE EASY RESTAURANT
BILL-DODGING BETCHA

The bet

I've just been reading about a new restaurant on the moon. It
has great food but no atmosphere. Perhaps the best restaurant
atmosphere back down here on earth is at Noma, which was
named the best restaurant in the world not so long ago. It
certainly lists some fascinating dishes on its menu, including
live ants, wriggling prawn and fried moss.

But this is nothing compared to Guo-li-zhuang, a restaurant on the delightfully named Dongsishitiao Street in Beijing. This is China's first penis restaurant. According to Chinese 'experts', eating penises is good for a man's sexual potency and is said to improve a lady's complexion, though women are advised not to bite off more than they can chew.

At Guo-li-zhuang you can treat yourself, among other delicacies, to mouth-watering horse, snake and duck willies. I wonder if *coq au vin* is on the menu. I know they offer blue whale penis, which is eight feet long and costs about £330. It sounds quite a mouthful – I'm guessing it's a dish for sharing.

The fried and flambéed steamed yak penis also sounds interesting, as do the sheep's testicles on a bed of curry. You can get boiled testicles too, not from spending too long in a hot bath, but cooked for you by the waitress in a tasty broth. For the truly inquisitive, there's even a hotpot of penises of ten different kinds.

For the less adventurous there's the simple penis-on-a-stick, or 'Henry's whip', as it's apparently called. Or you could just go to McDonald's.

Here's a betcha that's great for any restaurant. Although it sounds like evens, your victim cannot win this bet unless he understands what's going on.

Let's suppose you are out for a meal with a friend and after three courses and some coffee it's finally time to pay the bill. You offer a bet with a 50/50 chance that your chum will not have to pay anything and you'll be landed with the entire bill. What you do is hand your friend a box of matches and ask him or her to drop any number of them into your hand. If they then want to add or take any away they may. The number of matches is an entirely free choice.

Once they are happy, you break the matches in half – completely fairly, there's no funny business – and drop them into an ashtray, or onto the tablecloth. You now explain that you

are each going to take a broken matchstick in turn, and the one
with the last piece will pay the bill. Unless the matches have
been counted, which I don't recommend, neither of you knows
how many there are. But you still know you are going to win.

If you proceed exactly as you've said, with no monkey business, your friend will always be left with the last match. There's
no cheating – you do exactly what you said you'd do.

––––––––––

The chicanery

It is an interesting arithmetical fact that any number you
double will give you an even number, whether it is itself odd or
even. One doubled gives you two, two doubled gives you four,
three gives you six, seven gives you fourteen, ten gives you 20,
39 gives you 78, 4,155 gives you 8,310, 5,000,006 gives you
10,000,012. This simple, even dull, property of doubling is the
basis of this delightful betcha.

No matter how many matches your friend chooses, by
breaking them in half you double their number, guaranteeing
an even number of broken matches. All you need to do to
leave your chum with the last match, *and the bill*, is to pick the
first piece.

THINKING OUTSIDE THE BOX

The bet

There was a fellow on the news the other day who kept saying
'going forward' and 'iconic' and 'thinking outside the box'. He
also kept describing something or other as the 'most unique'
thing of its sort. He said 'most unique' about nine times. Then
he said 'completely unique' and I switched him off.

If something is unique there's only one of it, so you can't have a 'most unique' or 'completely unique' anything. However, it did strike me that this betcha contains an item so remarkable that you might feel that it really could be described as the most unique thing in the world.

What you do is bring out a small, mysterious-looking box. It is covered in cabalistic carvings of snakes and whatnot, or maybe sequins and glitter. If you've got some hoop earrings, a turban and a crystal ball these will help sell the idea.

There is a little keyhole in the box and you produce a tiny key and begin to tell your tale. 'Inside this magic box,' you say, 'is a unique item. So singular is it that nobody has ever seen it, not even me. But tonight I'm betting you that, not only will you be the first person ever to see this unique object, but, once you have seen it, nobody will ever see it again. If you're prepared to stand me a drink I will give you the magic key that unlocks the box. What do you say?'

You can bet £1, a drink, your shirt, or whatever you like. The answer is so delightful that you might even get £1 as well as the drink. And the whole thing (after the box) will set you back less than a penny.

The chicanery

First get yourself a fancy container, about the size of a Rubik's Cube. The words charity shop, car boot sale and eBay come to mind. It needn't have a lock, but if it does, so much the better. I've seen alluring lockable boxes going cheap on the internet. If it's insufficiently fancy then spend a little time tarting it up. This is where your untapped creativity comes in.

In an emergency you can contain your unique mystery object in a twisted paper napkin.

Next, buy yourself a bag of peanuts roasted in their shells (monkey nuts). Supermarkets and the internet have these at about a fiver for a 2lb bag, which should last you a lifetime, if you don't eat them.

Now put one of the shells (containing two nuts) into your box and shut the lid. Lock it if you can.

When you are ready, bring out the box and key, and, as moodily as you are able, tell your story of the esoteric experiments of the alchemists of yore, whose search for the so-called 'philosopher's stone' that would transmute base metals into gold ended in the creation of modern chemistry but never got anywhere near the gold.

'Yet in this box,' you say, 'I have something more precious than gold. More precious even than the Star of Africa diamond, and rarer than a taxi on a Saturday night in Soho. I bet you a double Scotch, or dinner [depends on who you're talking to], that in this box is an object so rare, so uncommon, so extraordinary, scarce, strange and subtle that nobody has ever seen it before. So singular is it that even I have never seen it. Its whole existence has been spent in darkness, waiting for you to look at it. You will be the first person in the world ever to see it. But more than this, as soon as you have seen it it will disappear from the world forever. It will cease to exist and nobody will ever see it again.'

Now this is a good story, and most people will be so intrigued that they will cough up the bet. Take the money, and slowly – for dramatic purposes – unlock and open the box. As soon as you take out the monkey nut the truth will dawn on your victim and they will probably laugh at the pedestrian nature of the object you produce from this fancy container.

Crumble the shell at one end and remove the seed. 'There it is,' you say. 'You are the first person ever to see that. Nobody has ever seen it before. And now nobody will ever see it again.' With that, pop the nut into your mouth and chew it up.

It's a fun bet, this one. You have gone from the sublime to the amusingly ridiculous but you've also given your audience something interesting to think about. Which, let's face it, is what it's all about.

THE SOLUTIONS

___

THE SAILOR WHO ATE THE CREAM TEA

Daisy realised that the man eating the cream tea in such a peculiar fashion was a sailor because he had his naval uniform on.

THE WISHING CUP OF KERIPUT

The mysterious inscription around the rim of the excavated pot is not Latin but English and is today thought to have been one of Lord Elpus's elaborate practical jokes. The legibility is compromised by some rather poor letter spacing, but when this is adjusted it clearly reads: IT IS A PISSPOT AND A BIG ONE.

MURDER IN THE SNOW

The fiery Ferrario is indeed the murderer. He has hatched a plot to do away with Trethewey, who is as he suspected taking liberties with his missus.

The first thing he did was to steal Trethewy's boots from his porch, an easy thing to accomplish since he lives next door. Two days later, after a fresh fall of snow and knowing that Trethewey will be heading off to the pub, probably in his moccasins again, Ferrario offers to carry him across the snowy field. He is already wearing his neighbour's monogrammed boots, which fit his small feet and look like any other boot once they are on. Trethewey accepts the offer.

Putting on a long coat, he conceals in the poacher's pocket his sawn-off shotgun. He has previously hidden his own boots in the copse.

He lifts his victim onto his broad back and as they cross the field he inevitably leaves a deeply marked impression of Trethewey's monogrammed boots behind him in the fresh snow, deeper in fact than the much lighter Trethewey could have made. There is, of course, only one set of tracks in the snow.

Halfway across, Ferrario reaches under his coat, swiftly pulls out the gun, and, stretching behind himself, releases both barrels upwards at Trethewey's face. The shot takes off the handsome features of the interloper, killing him at the same time.

Ferrario continues on his way, inevitably leaving less heavy prints as he strides to the edge of the field without Trethewey on his back. He goes on to the copse where he cleans himself up and buries the evidence. He then puts on his own boots, strolls to the pub and sits down to wait for his 'friend', who will never arrive.

THE YORKSHIRE FACTORY

Looking at the name S.GARTONS reflected in the stream Gerald realises that back-to-front the word reads SNOTRAG.S.

THE RIDDLE OF THE BURNS SUPPER

The coal, the carrot and the scarf are all that is left of the snowman that Julie and Jeremy made with the help of Suzanne the babysitter yesterday evening, while their parents were out. It snowed in the afternoon and there was just enough for them to make a snowman. Jeremy found an old scarf in a box of rags in the cellar, along with a few lumps of coal for his eyes, smile and buttons. The carrot came from the kitchen.

After the children went to bed a heavy rain began falling. It kept up till gone midnight, washing away much of the snowman. The morning's sun did the rest, leaving the strange objects on the Jones's snowless lawn.

Getting out of their taxi and coming up the garden path in the dark, Mr and Mrs Jones couldn't see the melting snowman. In any case they were not in much of a state to see anything.

Please drink responsibly.

THE ANNOYING COMPUTER PASSWORD

Bill spelt 'his password' the same way as everybody else: H I S P A S S W O R D. This is one of the best lateral thinking puzzles for reading out to friends. It is better read out than written down because to be absolutely fair when written down 'his password' should have inverted commas around it. But there you go – who said life was fair?

TERRY'S GIRLFRIENDS

The eastbound 'Emma' train leaves Terry's station once an hour, on the hour. The westbound 'Wendy' train also leaves once an hour, but at five past the hour, just five minutes later. Now what does this mean?

What it means is that although there are exactly as many westbound trains as eastbound trains – one every hour – there is a huge gap of fifty-five minutes between the westbound train leaving and the eastbound train arriving. Whatever time Terry arrives at the station during this fifty-five-minute period the next train will always be eastbound. On the other hand the gap between the eastbound train leaving and the westbound train arriving is only five minutes. So to catch a westbound train Terry must arrive at the station during this very brief slot, and, since he is arriving at the station at random times, this is most unlikely to happen. Terry is therefore almost certain to catch an eastbound train and very unlikely to catch a westbound train, which is why Wendy West is sick of waiting for him. Actually Emma East is also sick of him, but only because he leaves his dirty socks everywhere and never picks up the bath mat.

THE LORRY DRIVER SLAYING

The police did not let every person off scot-free, only the men. They arrested the dealer, who continued to admit her crime, and they charged her with murder. She was sent to Holloway Prison for a very long stretch.

THE MAGIC BUCKET

Stu has a swimming pool. To do his demonstration he puts on his swimming trunks and gets in, Laverne hands him the bucket, and he does everything with the bucket under water. When he's finished, he hands it out to her, still full of water.

THE IMPOSSIBLE BROTHERS

The brothers are, in fact, two of three triplets. The third triplet is called Roger, in case you care. The answer could, of course, have involved quadruplets, or any kind of multiple birth you care to think of. So if you worked out the essence of the problem award yourself a gold star.

ARMS AND THE CHILD

The children Margaret teaches are in the reception class and are only six years old. The children in Jenny's class are in the top year and are therefore older and, on average, taller, with correspondingly long arms. Write it out a hundred times.

THE WINDOW CLEANER IN THE SKY

Horace Morris lived in a flat on the 40th floor of the Alto Tower. He was cleaning the inside of his windows and standing on a chair to do so. When he slipped he fell onto the carpet, sustaining the kind of injuries a 60-year-old man might expect.

THE TROUBLESOME SIGNPOST

I was able to discount two possible directions without reference to the sign. I thought it most unlikely that I would continue ahead in a straight line, or Arthur would have said so. It also seemed ludicrous to go back to Brooksbridge, the way I'd already come.

Next I realised that although the signpost was horizontal its fingers were still pointing the correct way *in relation to one another*. I noticed that Rotherborough was to the left of, and at right angles to, the sign pointing to Brookbridge, from where I had just come. So I realised that standing with Brookbridge behind me I must make a left turn at the crossroads to get myself to Rotherborough.

I turned left and within fifteen minutes saw the bronze sculpture of Betty la Roche ahead of me, with Arthur waiting underneath, whistling a merry tune. We rather overdid our lunch in the Plasterers' Arms and I was obliged after our meeting to get a taxi back to the station.

THE KNIGHTSBRIDGE BARBER

Mr Teasy-Weasy said he would rather cut the hair of three Cockney women than one Yorkshirewoman because he would earn three times as much money.

THE FASTEST BEARD IN THE WORLD

Sean and his family lived in Barrow in Alaska. It is the USA's northernmost city and is located above the Arctic Circle. When the sun sets there in the winter it doesn't rise again for two months. That's plenty of time for a chap to grow a decent beard.

THE HIGH WINDOW

The bottom of the window in question was, as Ms Scrunt put it, 'almost eight feet from the floor'. Mr Snarbes, at five feet ten, is just shy of six feet. What he did when he heard the argument in the street was get the wooden chair that had been used to hold the door shut, put it against the wall, and stand on its back, the top of which was a standard three feet from the floor. This put his eyes at about eight feet six, halfway up the window, enabling him to see Joe Slepkava committing the crime.

THE CONFUSING COACH TRIP

If you remember, you were asked to, 'Imagine that ... *you* are driving a large charabanc ...' Therefore, to decide how many siblings the driver has, you need only count your own brothers and sisters, if you have any.

THE PILOT WHO WORE A DRESS

When asked what he would do if, after a long-haul flight, he met the captain wearing a dress in the hotel bar, the young trainee pilot answered the question like this: 'I would buy her a drink.' He thus revealed to his examiners that he had no prejudices about female pilots, and would get on well with any of them he met.

PICKING UP THE CHILDREN FROM SCHOOL

Sue and her children live in an old people's home because they are old people. Very old. Sue is 99 years old and her twins are 78. It's true that their father ran off with his secretary, but that was in 1960. The pictures of handsome film stars on Mitzi's wall are of Cary Grant and Gregory Peck. The twins were asked to give a talk on the Second World War because they were school-age children at the time and it's well known around the town that they have lots of stories of the bombs landing in their street, which they enjoy telling people at the bus stop.

Time to take the teeth out and push along to bed.

THE CAR IN THE RIVER

The car had crashed into the River Greta, which is at points fast-flowing but at many points also quite shallow. At some places you can wade across it if you're clever.

THE SAD END OF FELICITY FFOLKES

Felicity had been waved through into the safari park by a dozy fool smoking a mind-altering cigarette. So absent-minded was she that she had hired a convertible and was taking pictures with the top down. The lion simply lifted her out and had his lunch.

Please drive safely.

THE BLIND BEGGAR

'The blind beggar' is one of my all-time favourite problems. It is short, simple to understand, without any cheats or confusing detail, and it relies on lateral thinking and nothing else. The clue to the puzzle is that not all beggars, and not all blind people, are male. Indeed, although the two characters in this problem are not brothers, they *are* siblings, because the blind beggar is a woman. The pair are therefore brother and sister.

A BIRTHDAY MESSAGE FROM THE QUEEN

Though Charlie Trimble celebrated reaching his 100th year in 2015 he was at that time only 99 and wouldn't have *lived* for a hundred years until 2016. This is because anyone's first year of life is 'year zero' not 'year 1'. You are no years old in your first year and only reach your 100th birthday in your 101st year. Hope that's clear.

TALKING RUBBISH

The environmentally damaging items that are usually thrown away carelessly, without being put into a plastic bin liner first, are plastic bin liners.

THE FLOOD

Moses took no animals on the ark, because he wasn't on it. That would have been Noah.

HOSPITAL ASSAULT

Mr Cutwell is a consultant obstetric surgeon. His patient is Mrs Sara Stansbeard, who is about to have a Caesarian section delivery of her son Wilfred. As he delivers the baby, Mr Cutwell smacks Wilfred's bottom to provoke the first breath. This procedure is no longer recommended, but Mr Cutwell, who is a successful doctor with thousands of grateful patients behind him, is old fashioned.

THE TWO ITALIANS

The Italians, who are both successful professionals with strong academic backgrounds, are husband and wife.

HOUSE PAINTING MADE SIMPLE

The two Franks have done exactly as Junior suggested. They have painted just one side of the house – the *outside*.

THE ABSENT-MINDED TAXI DRIVER

The policeman took little notice of the taxi driver going the wrong way down a one-way street because the taxi driver was walking.

PLANE CRASH IN NO MAN'S LAND

The chaplains decided that, all in all, it would be better not to bury the survivors, who they felt might not like it. Instead they buried just the dead.

THE STRANGE STORY OF ANTONY AND CLEOPATRA

Antony and Cleopatra are the owner's goldfish. They died when his boisterous dog knocked their fish bowl onto the tile floor.

Incidentally, in case you were wondering, 'BCE' is a religiously neutral term dating from 1708 that stands for 'Before the Common Era'. Scholars increasingly prefer it to 'BC' – 'Before Christ'.

BIRD STRIKE

The flight on which the bird strike accident happened to Ruby was the last one. Don't forget, it killed her, so her opportunity for flying aeroplanes after that one was severely limited.

CONTRADICTIO IN ADJECTO

The solicitor told my friend that it is illegal under English law for a man to marry his widow's sister – *because he is dead.*

UNCONSCIOUS SEXISM

Practised lateral thinkers might well have got this one early on. It depends on our fondness for making assumptions about a person's sex based on their profession. Most police officers are men, and some are no doubt sexist pigs. But in this case the traffic officer was a woman.

The motorcyclist's shaded helmet had obscured her face and it was only at the moment when she spoke that the driver realised her mistake.

So it wasn't the police officer in this case who was unconsciously sexist, it was the woman driver. In fact, if *you* also thought that the police officer was a man then you too could be accused of this fault. It is a matter for you and your conscience. I'm not getting involved. These arguments are hard to win and I've got a bottle to open.

THE SHORT WEEK

Friday was the name of Nemo's horse.

THE MAN IN THE LIFT

'The man in the lift' is without question the archetypal lateral thinking mystery and it is perhaps the best known. The answer to the problem is simple, as it is in the best lateral thinking mysteries. Gordon Gordon is of uncommonly short stature, and for this reason, though he can easily reach the lift button for the ground floor he is unable to reach higher than the seventh-floor button, so he is obliged to get out and walk the last three floors.

Apart from the bother of the lift, Gordon Gordon doesn't give two hoots about being short. He's one of those people with what satirical doctors have named 'proctoheliosis', that is to say, he thinks the sun shines out of his bum.

MARY'S MUM

It's easy to forget that this story is not about Mary but about Mary's mum. If Mary's mum has four daughters then three of them will be Mary's sisters, April, May, and June. The fourth daughter, of course, is Mary herself. One thing's for sure, she isn't called July.

THE DESERTED PRAIRIE CABIN

With a candle, an oil lamp and some firewood but only one match, Hudson Flint should first light *the match*.

THE TWO PRIME MINISTERS

Winston Churchill was Prime Minister twice, from 1940 to 1945 and from 1951 to 1955. He had the same parents all his life. No wonder he looked so much like himself.

THE TEA-LEAF

One of the most ingenious and influential crime stories ever written, *The Tea-leaf*, 1925, contains a brilliant idea cleverly concealed by the character of the protagonists and the unusual environment of the crime.

The secret concerns a wrinkle commonly employed by 'impossible' murder authors and lateral thinking puzzlers. It is to do with the difference in the properties of water in its solid and liquid states.

The answer to the puzzle lies in the odd presence of a thermos flask in a Turkish bath. The tea-leaf in the wound links the weapon with the flask. The only plausible way you can explain the tea-leaf is that it came out of the flask sticking to the point of the dagger, and was then driven into the wound. But a flask, of course, can not only keep things hot – it can also keep things cold. Gradually the mist begins to clear.

The scientist Kelstern has manufactured a weapon in the form of an icicle, in a premeditated plot to kill himself and put the blame on his enemy Willoughton. He has, as we learn, been suffering from cancer and, we may guess, is facing death whatever happens. In the original story the weapon is made from solid carbon dioxide, which is harder than water ice, but this is not a critical point.

Another clue to motive lies in the furious emotions of the two men. Kelstern puts the deadly icicle into his flask, takes it with him to the Turkish bath, where he knows Willoughton will be, initiates a flaming row and once his enemy has left the room opens the flask and stabs himself in the heart. Whereupon the weapon miraculously disappears, melting away in the extreme heat.

He has committed suicide in a cunning and spiteful effort to hang his enemy Willoughton, and has nearly succeeded. Only his carelessness in washing out the thermos leads to the discovery of the crime.

THE ADVENTURE OF
THE SPECKLED BAND

The Speckled Band, 1892, is one of four Sherlock Holmes stories that can be classed as 'locked-room' mysteries. It was Arthur Conan Doyle's own favourite.

The guilty suspect from the outset is Dr Grimesby Roylott, who is motivated to murder his stepdaughters by the fear of losing money to them upon their marriage. His training in medicine and his life in India come together with his penchant for exotic animals to provide one of the weirdest methods of murder in all fiction.

As Holmes and Watson look at the dead body of Dr Roylott, the speckled band around his head begins to move. And rearing up from his hair is the diamond-shaped head of a swamp adder, the deadliest snake in India. He has died within ten seconds of being bitten.

Holmes catches the snake with the adapted lash and throws it back into the safe, where it had been kept. Miss Stoner has had a lucky escape.

As they return to London, Holmes explains the solution.

A dummy bell rope next to an immovable bed instantly suggested to him that the rope was merely a bridge for something passing through the fake ventilator, and the idea of a snake was an obvious one. But it would have to be recalled so Dr Roylott trained it to return when summoned by his whistle, probably by use of the milk. He would put the adder through the ventilator knowing that it would crawl down the rope onto the bed beside his stepdaughter, who sooner or later must fall victim.

Holmes tells Watson that during their vigil he was ready with his cane. As soon as he heard the creature hiss he lit the light and attacked it, driving it back through the ventilator, where it turned upon its master.

'In this way,' says Sherlock Holmes, 'I am no doubt indirectly responsible for Dr Grimesby Roylott's death, and I cannot say that it is likely to weigh very heavily upon my conscience.'

THE GLASS COFFIN

To discover how Sir Herbert Hardcastle has died, let us first eliminate the impossible. There is no way out of the room once it is locked, therefore whoever killed Sir Herbert must still be in the conservatory. The conservatory has been searched and there is nobody in it except for Sir Herbert. It follows, then, that either he killed himself – deliberately, or by mistake – or that an accident happened to him.

Using Occam's razor, the principle that the simplest theory is the best bet, we may assume that things have been done in the following order. 1) Sir Herbert enters the conservatory as usual and locks the door behind him, 2) he tends to his flowers as always, 3) at 5.20, his normal time, he closes the ceiling ventilators using the long pole to pull them shut.

Closing the vents is the last thing he always did before leaving the conservatory for the day so it must have been after he shut them that he died.

The nature of his head wound makes suicide practically impossible, therefore an accident must have happened to him. What was it, then, that hit him or fell on top of his head? The clue to this lies in two things: the hook in Sir Herbert's tea, which is the broken-off business end of the vent-opening pole, and the unusual position of this pole, upside-down on the coconut matting.

The rusty hook is not heavy enough to kill even a 92-year-old man, but the pole definitely is, especially if it struck his head end-on. We know that the hook has broken off the pole, and Sir Herbert would not have put it in his tea; it can only have dropped in there. Now we begin to see the truth.

Sir Herbert entered the conservatory, locking the door behind him as usual to avoid disturbance. He tended to his orchids and at 5.20 took the pole from its clip, held it up, and slipped the hook into the ring on the frame of the ventilator window.

He pulled hard on the pole but the vent was too stiff. So, stretching out his arms and staring at his boots, he gave a final tug. At this point the ventilator window suddenly came free and shut with a bang, a noise heard by the housemaid. The rusty hook sheared off with the impact, and dropped with a splash into Sir Herbert's half-finished cup of tea. The pole, under the force of gravity and Sir Herbert's final pull, struck him hard, in the centre of the crown of his straw hat, then slid down the back of his neck, where it was caught by his shirt collar, which stopped its descent. The hook end was now falling faster than the blunt end and it was the hook end, minus its hook, that landed on the coconut matting, which held it fast as the blunt end shot out of Sir Herbert's shirt and was thrown against the trunk of the banana tree, where it came to rest, as if casually leant there. All this happened in a flash, as the already dead body of Sir Herbert fell to the floor.

What a way to go.

A GAME OF ROULETTE

Sigismund Firthkettle is the pen name of Arturo Willis (1900–1985). *A Game of Roulette* is typical of his style.

Jackson has been the victim of a poisoning technique once much loved by agents of US Intelligence. It is known as 'aspirin roulette'. In the old days, agents would break into a victim's house while he was out, go into the bathroom, open the medicine cupboard and drop a poison pill into a bottle of aspirin.

The beauty of this technique is that the set-up might predate the death by days, weeks or months. All that was required was for the victim one day to take an aspirin and, bang!, he would drop dead at home. It's rather like Russian roulette, only quieter, with no clue left to find.

Now that painkillers come in little packets the technique has changed. The way Bunce did it was to sneak into Jackson's office, having been tipped off by Fernsby Intaglio's director that he was outside, smoking a cigarette in the sunshine. Jackson had left his jacket on the back of his chair. In the pocket was a box of his usual aspirin and it was the work of but a moment for Bunce to take one of the carefully set-up foil packets made by the security services' dirty-tricks department and switch it for the ordinary one. This new insert looked just like the supermarket one but contained a single deadly pill along with seven ordinary aspirins.

Then it was just a matter of time.

The poison of choice was saxitoxin, a fast-acting and very powerful shellfish toxin that causes so-called 'paralytic shellfish poisoning'. Deadly even in small doses, saxitoxin's symptoms can appear just ten minutes after ingestion. These include nausea, vomiting, tingling arms and legs, slurred speech, a choking sensation, breathing problems, unconsciousness, and death.

By the way, I bet you tried to lick your elbow.

THE TWO BOTTLES OF RELISH

The Two Bottles of Relish, 1932, is a firm favourite with impossible murder fans. It has wit, simplicity, and a shock ending that was quite a thing in 1932, when it was first published.

An Inspector Ulton comes to the flat to hear Linley's solution to the mystery of Nancy Elth. He and Ulton go into his bedroom for a quiet discussion, so Smithers never hears Linley's answer to the problem, but guesses it from his last words to the inspector.

As he is leaving, Ulton turns to ask Linley why Steeger cut down the trees. Linley tells him that he did it to get an appetite.

Put this remark together with the two bottles of relish bought by a vegetarian, but intended to spice up meat, and you have the unappetising solution to this intriguing and delightful mystery.

THE PROBLEM OF THOR BRIDGE

The Problem of Thor Bridge, 1922, is one of Arthur Conan Doyle's last Sherlock Holmes stories, and one of the most difficult for the lateral thinking reader to solve. Intriguingly the tale includes shadows of Conan Doyle's own infidelity with a younger woman. In any case, it is a terrific plot and the solution to the mystery is as compelling as the problem.

To test his theory, Holmes conducts an experiment. Watson and he go to Thor Bridge, where he ties a large stone to a length of string and attaches this to Watson's service revolver. He lowers the stone over the parapet of the bridge so that it hangs clear above the water. He then stands on the fatal spot, some distance from the edge of the bridge, with the gun in his hand, the string being taut between the weapon and the heavy stone on the farther side.

He raises the pistol to his head, and lets go his grip. In an instant the gun is whisked away by the weight of the stone, striking the underside of the parapet with a sharp crack before vanishing over the side into the water, and leaving a second chip of the exact size and shape as the first.

Using a grappling hook the police drag up Watson's gun together with the murder weapon, which is tied to a stone in the same way. With this gun a vindictive Mrs Gibson has attempted to disguise her own suicide and fasten a charge of murder upon an innocent victim. Miss Dunbar has been vindicated.

The method was simple. First Miss Gibson demanded a meeting with Miss Dunbar and kept her note confirming the time and place. Holmes points out that in her anxiety that it should be discovered, 'she somewhat overdid it by holding it in her hand to the last'. She then took one of her husband's revolvers and kept it for her own use, hiding the second of the pair in Miss Dunbar's wardrobe after discharging one barrel in the woods without attracting attention.

At the appointed time she went down to the bridge and when Miss Dunbar appeared she poured out her hatred. The governess fled back to the house, and once she was out of hearing Mrs Gibson put the stone in place and fired the gun. It was whisked out of her hand and over the parapet, sinking to the bottom as she fell dead upon her back.

'I do not think that in our adventures we have ever come across a stranger example of what perverted love can bring about,' muses Holmes.

ARSENIC AND OLD LUCE

On analysis the arsenic-containing flakes in the dust from the ambassador's room were found to be particles of old green paint. Attention turned at once to the ornate ceiling, agitated every morning by the washing machine upstairs. The ceiling had been painted years before with what was found to be an arsenic-rich green pigment. This flaking paint, shaken off every morning by the shuddering washing machine, had been falling for months into Clare Boothe Luce's food and drink, building up a cumulative dose of the deadly poison.

The ceiling was redecorated but the exhausted ambassador decided to retire from the job. Back in the United States her health and abrasive wit recovered. She died in Washington in 1987 at the age of 84.

THE RATHER-SHORT-VERY-LONG BASEBALL GAME

The secret behind this delightful muddle is that the crew had broken surface near the North Pole in a stretch of open water surrounded by thick sea ice as far as the eye could see. Captain McLaren describes a light blanket of snow, with, here and there, small pools of meltwater refrozen into glass-like ice.

By deliberately siting the pitcher's mound directly over the Pole, the men had created a situation in which, owing to the lines of longitude meeting at the Pole and making a nonsense of the notion of today and tomorrow, a batter hitting a home run would circumnavigate the globe and pass through 24 time zones.

If he hit a ball into right field it would fly across the international dateline and land in tomorrow. When the right fielder caught the flyball, it was already the next day where he was, so the batter couldn't be considered out for a further 24 hours.

If the batter had hit a line drive, that is a sharply hit low-flying ball, into right field and a fielder had thrown it to second or third base it would have landed back in the day of play. Or yesterday, as far as he was concerned. A ball hit to left field would remain in the same day but if it was caught and thrown to first base it could go into tomorrow, depending on where the first baseman was standing.

Action around second base could take several days to complete for the same reasons.

It was a good job Captain McLaren and the *Seadragon* crew didn't decide to continue playing till dark, because at that time of year at the North Pole it's daytime all night.

THE CURIOUS CASE OF
DIHYDROGEN MONOXIDE

Dihydrogen monoxide is just another name for water (H_2O), which has two hydrogen molecules (dihydrogen) and one oxygen molecule (monoxide). Yes, it can be dangerous, but without it we'd all be dead. The director of DHMO.org is Dr Tom Way, Associate Professor of Computer Science at Villanova University, in Pennsylvania. His satirical website is designed to encourage people to add an appropriate dollop of scepticism to scientific-sounding scare-stories and think twice – not to say laterally – before swallowing bucket-loads of unnerving facts.

THE *MARY CELESTE* AFFAIR

To answer the *Mary Celeste* problem, you have to come at it sideways.

Despite the confusing mass of evidence, everything about the eerie case of this abandoned 'ghost ship' suggests a well-ordered, if rapid, departure in the lifeboat. It is highly suggestive that most of the ship's important papers, along with the captain's navigational instruments, had been taken. If there's one thing you need in a lifeboat, it's navigational tools.

But for a captain and his crew to abandon a seaworthy ship for a small lifeboat in such a rush, something imminently dangerous must have threatened them.

It seems unlikely that the crew would leave the ship with only 3.5 feet of water in the hold, which they seemed to be pumping out. They were aware that this amount of water was not threatening the boat. It is even less likely that a drunk or mutinous crew would bloodlessly kill the captain and officers and then leave in a small lifeboat.

It is true that fumes from the denatured alcohol could have caused quite an explosion. Professor Andrea Sella of University

College London built a model of the hold of *Mary Celeste* for a television programme using paper cartons for the alcohol barrels. He created a gas explosion that caused a pressure-wave and a large fireball that left no scorch marks. Had this happened on the ship it would still have blasted the crew sideways, but would they have abandoned ship after the bang?

My favourite answer to the problem is the one proposed by Captain David Williams. He suggests that after the crew had taken a break from the unremitting heavy weather by anchoring on the leeward side of Santa Maria Island, the Captain gave orders to get under way again and the crew went back to pumping the bilge of its 3.5 feet of water, and unfurling the sails.

Once under way, the sea floor beneath *Mary Celeste* was suddenly torn by a vigorous shallow earthquake, which vibrated the ocean and shook the ship fiercely up and down. So violent was this quake that the iron deck stove was thrown into the air, coming down outside the chocks that normally kept it from sliding about. The large drinking-water vessel was likewise bounced loose on the main deck, and the ship's wooden compass stand was knocked over, breaking its housing.

Up in the rigging the sailors setting the foresail and topsails could have been jolted into the sea, leaving the fore-lower topsail only partly set. Some of the other rigging was left hanging loose for the same reason. Even in a breeze improperly set loose sails could have been torn away within a few days.

The men pumping out the bilge were knocked over by the terrifying seaquake, abandoning the sounding rod and bilge valve on the deck. The barrels of alcohol in the hold were savagely thrown around, spilling some 500 gallons into the bilge.

With fumes from the ruptured barrels now filling the hold, the crew, fearful of an explosion, opened the remaining hatches and skylights to ventilate the lower decks. They could not open the main hatch because the lifeboat was still lashed to its cover.

As the alarming quake continued, the *Mary Celeste* looked and felt as though she would be shaken to bits. The Captain gave orders to abandon ship. His wife and daughter went into the lifeboat, and the crew followed. So rushed and fearful were they that an axe was used to sever the ropes lashing the lifeboat to the main hatch.

Into the water went the boat and it began to drift away from the *Mary Celeste* out into the ocean just as the seaquake was subsiding.

In May of the following year the *Liverpool Daily Albion* reported that two rafts had been found off the coast of Spain. Tied on were five very decomposed bodies, one wrapped in an American flag. Had the *Mary Celeste's* lifeboat come to pieces and been reassembled as two rafts?

Whether it was a seaquake that caused the captain and crew of the *Mary Celeste* to abandon ship, it must have been something as rapid and terrifying. It probably wasn't aliens in flying saucers. In the end, exactly what happened to the unlucky ship is a question of probability, because, in the words of the old proverb, 'The sea never gives up her secrets.'

THE STORY OF BIG BEN

The number of hands on the clock of Big Ben is eight. Don't forget, there are four faces to the clock, and each has two hands.

THE EUSTON ROAD POISONINGS

At University College Hospital Professor Charles Rimmington had an idea. The very unusual time lag before symptoms emerged in these three patients suggested that this was an extremely rare case of cantharidin poisoning. If renal symptoms developed in these patients, then it would confirm his diagnosis.

Cantharidin, or Spanish fly, is a very powerful and dangerous irritant obtained from the iridescent crushed bodies of so-called 'blister beetles', which live in scrublands and woods throughout southern Europe, Central Asia and Siberia. It is used today mainly in creams for removing warts, but its chief historic use was as an aphrodisiac.

Spanish fly has been used in love potions since classical times. When taken in minute amounts cantharidin irritates the genitals, resulting in increased blood flow that resembles the engorgement of sexual arousal. The sensations provoked were long ago believed to enhance a woman's awareness of her genitalia, and arouse an urgent need for sexual intercourse. In men, Spanish fly was said to result in prolonged and prize-winning erections.

This was the chemical that Professor Rimmington suspected had poisoned the three people, and, as he had predicted, the day after their first symptoms both female patients began to suffer renal failure. Their conditions worsened rapidly and by the end of the day both had died. Post mortems confirmed corrosive poisoning. The professor's inspired guess was correct. After further forensic work, minute amounts of cantharidin were found in both bodies.

The police, who had their chief suspect, went to University College Hospital to break the news of the typists' deaths to the office manager. When he heard this he broke down and cried out, 'Oh my God! Why didn't somebody tell me?' On the way to the police station he said, 'I am to blame. I don't know what made me do it.'

Under questioning, he agreed that he had taken some cantharidin from the pharmacist's office, having heard of Spanish fly's aphrodisiac effects when he was in the army. He put a little on the coconut ice using a pair of scissors.

His target was, he said, the older typist, with whom he had been having a long, romantic, though sexless, affair. 'She kept saying she would let me do it next time. When the next time came I made up my mind to give her cantharidin to stimulate her desire for me.'

The man denied giving any to the younger woman and couldn't explain how she had been poisoned. His own blistered face was apparently the result of careless contamination by his fingers.

At the Central Criminal court the office manager pleaded guilty to two charges of manslaughter and was sentenced to five years' imprisonment.

KENTUCKY BLUES

The Fugate family tree was traced back to 1820, when Frenchman Martin Fugate emigrated from his homeland to Kentucky. No record of the man's skin colour existed but Cawein suspected that he had been carrying the blue gene. Fugate married Elizabeth Smith, a non-blue local woman who, against all the odds, also carried the recessive gene. They had seven children. Four of them were blue. That's where the trouble started.

For 200 years six generations of the Blue Fugates lived in the same remote area of Kentucky, cut off from the outside world and without roads. The people of Ball Creek and the aptly named Troublesome Creek were so short of suitable marriage partners that, over the years, the isolated inhabitants started families with members of other families nearby, including the Combses and the Ritchies, and inadvertently began to have offspring with other blue-gene-carrying members of their own families, including cousins, and other blood relations.

But as the remote areas of the United States became increasingly developed, the Blue People took to Kentucky's newly built roads for the first time. They began driving away from their communities to settle in far-flung places and marry strange new people. The blue gene soon began to be diluted among these new genetically dissimilar families, and its effects gradually died away. Benjamin Stacy (born 1975) is the last known descendent of the Blue Fugates.

UNCLE BOB'S MAGIC PIPE

Uncle Bob's method for smoking a pipe in the rain was simple. He turned it upside down. It was quite happy the wrong way up and the tobacco continued to smoulder away cheerfully without falling out because, in burning, it formed an intact lump, attaching itself lightly to the wall of the pipe. Uncle Bob said that, in the street, a pipe was a great bird-puller, as all the huddled ladies he passed would glance across at him from under their brollies and murmur, 'Oh, what a lovely manly aroma.'

THE INCREDIBLE STORY OF KASPAR HAUSER

If you think about the problem for a minute, it soon becomes apparent the kind of person the mysterious Kaspar Hauser was.

When the note in the blue bag was examined it was found to contain spelling and grammatical errors typical of Hauser's own. It was folded with strange diagonal folds, characteristic of the unusual method habitually used by Hauser himself. This led the court of enquiry to conclude that his story about being attacked was fantasy and that he had stabbed himself.

Indeed, all of Kaspar Hauser's tales seem very unlikely. There were never any witnesses to his misfortunes, and many of those trying to care for him found him self-obsessed and habitually untruthful. The purported razor attack must be the only case in history where the victim has been set upon while on the toilet.

His account of accidentally picking up a gun and shooting himself after being reproached for lying – a very touchy subject, you might think – beggars belief. Mrs Biberbach, in whose house this happened, remarked on Kaspar Hauser's 'horrid deceitfulness' and 'duplicity'. Others reported that he was extravagantly untruthful.

Kaspar Hauser, whoever he really was, seems to have wanted everybody to pay attention to him. Self-inflicted wounds – a classic ruse of unbalanced people who crave attention – tend to be made on the upper extremities, opposite the dominant hand. This is the position of the wounds received by Kaspar Hauser. The final knife wound was possibly just too enthusiastic.

In the end, this irresistible mystery has only probable answers. But, in this, it resembles almost all real-life questions.

THE GREAT EPPING JAUNDICE MYSTERY

Dr Kopelman visited the bedside of the five remaining Epping Jaundice patients in St Margaret's Hospital. He asked each of them if they remembered having eaten any wholemeal bread before becoming ill. Yes – every single one of them had recently bought and eaten a specific, expensive, speciality loaf from an Epping bakery, but many people had eaten it before without harm. What about the female patient who said she had only eaten white bread? Just then a staff nurse came rushing up. The woman had suddenly remembered buying a wholemeal loaf immediately before becoming ill.

The epidemic had two definite centres, one in Epping itself and the other in Chipping Ongar. It turned out that the Epping bakery had just opened a new branch in the village. Both shops were well run and hygienic but the manager could not be interviewed as he was in hospital with jaundice.

Dr Ash learned that the fancy wholemeal bread in question was bought mainly by well-off food connoisseurs, many of whom had been eating it for a long time without ill effects. But some kind of chemical poisoning appeared to be going on, and whatever it was acted fast and was very toxic to the liver.

Ash ordered production and sale of the bread to be stopped at once, though nothing out of the ordinary could be seen in the bakery. The only unusual ingredient was the wholemeal flour, which was delivered in sacks by a reliable firm.

A new sack of this flour had been tipped into the storage bins on 1 February and the first spoonfuls taken out for baking the same day. This sack of flour now became Isidore Ash's prime suspect, so samples were sent for analysis.

For the most part the flour seemed quite uncontaminated. However, flour from the storage bins did show a minuscule trace of an unidentifiable organic chemical, at just thirteen parts in a million, surely too small a concentration to cause jaundice.

Ash's attention turned to the delivery van.

The boss of the haulage firm said that their van carried different products, including liquids from a commercial chemist's. The driver remembered a plastic container tipping over on the day of delivery, and the top coming off. About a gallon of the chemical had spilled and some paper packages had been spoiled, but the sack of flour seemed to have been unaffected.

Then a telephone call was received from a lady who had heard reports of the suspect bread from the media. She had bought and tasted some of the bread and found it revoltingly bitter. She had thrown it out for the birds but they wouldn't eat it and it was still on her lawn, if anyone was interested. Samples were collected and sent to the National Toxicology Laboratory in Carshalton.

While Carshalton analysed the bread from the lawn, the pathologist at St Margaret's fed some to laboratory mice, who became jaundiced. He found that the chemical was present in the bread at quantities 200 times greater than the bread so far tested.

With results of the analyses coming in, the chemical company suggested a suspect substance. It seemed that the Epping Jaundice was the result of poisoning by something called 4,4'-Methylenedianiline (MDA), a chemical used in the making of polymers and as an epoxy resin hardener. MDA is now on the list of 'substances of very high concern' of the European Chemicals Agency.

The container being transported in the van had spilt but the liquid had been invisible against the brown sack, and on the dark brown flour. The sack had then stood in the warm bakery and was dry by the time it was tipped into the storage bins. The highly contaminated flour was at the bottom of the sack and went in last, ending up at the top of the bin. It was therefore the first to be used for baking.

And so the epidemic started, with the acute effects of poisoning showing up quickly. Five or six slices of the heavily contaminated bread were enough to produce liver damage. But by the time samples were taken for testing almost all of the poisoned flour had gone.

All the Epping Jaundice patients recovered over time.

THE FASTEST SUBMARINE IN THE WORLD

The USS *Skate* was travelling only two miles south of the North Pole. The distance around the world at that point is just twelve miles. That means, of course, that it managed to circumnavigate the globe while going a fair bit slower than a milk float ambling down a country lane.